CW00818959

The
Wine Producers'
Handbook

First published in 2018 by Posthouse Publishing Ltd
Volume © Posthouse Publishing 2018
Text © Belinda Kemp and Emma Rice 2018

Cover photograph © Marc Hill / Alamy Stock Photo
A CIP catalogue for this book is available from the British Library
ISBN 978 1 903872 30 7

All rights reserved. No part of this publication may be reproduced, stored in a retrieval system or transmitted in any form, or by any means, electronic or mechanical, including photocopying and recording, or by any information storage and retrieval system except as may be expressly permitted by the UK 1988 Copyright, Designs and Patents Act and the USA 1976 Copyright Act or in writing from the publisher. Requests for permission should be addressed to Posthouse Publishing Ltd, No 2 Cleat, St Margaret's Hope, South Ronaldsay, Orkney, KW17 2RW. The publishers have made every effort to ensure the accuracy of information in the book at the time of going to press. However, they cannot accept responsibility for any loss, injury or inconvenience resulting from the use of information contained in this book.

Publisher: Rupert Wheeler
Consulting editors: Paul Woodrow-Hill and Duncan McNeil
Editor: Ted Bruning
Printed in Great Britain by TJ International Ltd

Publisher's acknowledgements:
The publishers would like to thank Paul Woodrow-Hill and Duncan McNeil for their invaluable input and technical help in the publishing of this book and to Ted Bruning for his editorial assistance. The publishers would also like to thank WineGB for their assistance and to Simon Robinson, Chairman of Wine GB for his support.

The Wine Producers' Handbook

A practical guide to setting up a
vineyard and winery in Great Britain

Belinda Kemp & Emma Rice

Contents

Case Studies

Foreword

Production of wine in the UK has changed radically over the last few years and the industry is evolving very rapidly. It is not that many years ago that all producers were passionate people making wine on a small scale who wanted to prove that decent wine could be made from grapes grown here.

The advent of the larger sparkling wine producers and the success that they have enjoyed over the last 10-15 years or so has changed everything. There is now lots of evidence in numerous major international competitions over many years that not just good but truly great wines can be made here – indeed this year for the first time English and Welsh sparkling wines won more gold medals in the Sommelier Wine awards than champagne – the first time any region has achieved that.

There is an increasing number of larger commercial producers who are organised on lines some way removed from the earlier enthusiasts: indeed, two producers are companies whose shares are traded on a stock market. English and Welsh wine is far more widely available than it has ever been and the larger producers are exporting around the world.

Plumpton College has brought a new level of expertise and training to the UK so that it is increasingly becoming a career option for young (and not so young!) people. These are exciting times indeed in the UK industry and WineGB's recent survey has demonstrated that the rapid expansion currently being experienced – some three million vines were planted in the UK in 2015-8 – is likely to continue for some time.

But while the larger producers have expanded, the small producers continue to thrive and I expect that will continue to be the case for the foreseeable future, given that every other wine region in the world has a similar balance of large commercial production and smaller passionate artisanal producers. My expectation is that the next major development will be our still wines beginning to enjoy their day in the sun, and nobody would be more pleased about that than myself. Another feature of the UK industry is our passion for innovation and the fact that there has not historically been a large industry perhaps even helps as we are not bound with all the bureaucracy and history which so inhibits others.

Of course the elephant in the room at present is Brexit. WineGB has been heavily involved in making representations to the Government on this issue (see **www.winegb.co.uk/industry/winegb-response-to-government-consultations**/) which sets out our basic position on a number of topics, including any possible agreement with the EU, submissions to Parliamentary Committees regarding possible free trade deals and to DEFRA on the future of farming.

At the time of writing it was becoming increasingly possible that the UK will leave the EU without any agreement in place and consequently WineGB is considering issuing guidance to its members on what precautionary measures they might consider. Fundamentally we expect to recommend that members consider what they will need over the year following the UK's exit on 29 March 2019 (such as bottles, stillage cages etc) they need and, if they are exporters, consider whether they wish to join with other vineyards in pre-placing stock inside the EU to support their EU customers in a facility which WineGB is considering developing.

Investment in the English and Welsh wine industry has increased considerably in recent years reflecting the high quality of the wines being produced and the rapidly expanding market for it, both in the UK and overseas. Wine GB's survey of its members in early 2018 lead to the issue of its view on the future of the industry for the next 25 years and that paper, 'Looking to the Future', is also available on the WineGB website. The greatest challenge at present is probably ensuring winemaking capacity keeps up with the increase in the planted area.

This book is therefore a timely contribution to the industry literature and I commend it to all – large and small, still and sparkling!

Simon Robinson
Chairman, WineGB, October 2018

Introduction

It is commonly held that viticulture and winemaking were introduced to Britain by the Romans, whose conquest begun in 43AD. The British tribes folk who constituted the peasantry of Roman Britannia were in the main beer drinkers, but their native rulers quickly acquired the habits of civilisation and not only imported wine from Gaul and Spain but also started growing grapes themselves. It is speculated that today's Wrotham Pinot – found growing wild in the 1950s against a garden wall in Wrotham, Kent – is descended from Roman vines. Fittingly, seedlings have been planted at Fishbourne Roman villa near Chichester, West Sussex, once the palace of Cogidubnus, an early ally of Rome.

Whether the Wrotham Pinot (which is very similar to the Champagne grape Pinot Meunier) really does have Roman roots or not, there is plenty of archaeological evidence for viticulture in Roman Britain and documentary evidence for vineyards in Saxon England. Surveys in Northamptonshire have revealed evidence that suggests vineyards were established during the Roman occupation as deposits of grapevine pollen were found dating from that time. Research has shown that grapevines were planted in about 100AD at Bagden Farm, less than 350 yards from Denbies Estate in Surrey.

The adoption in 312 of Christianity as the Roman Empire's official religion created a new market for wine, as Mass could not be said without it. Much later Anglo-Saxon charters record wild and overgrown vines or 'wine-trees' – Roman relics? – as boundary markers. After the conversion of the Anglo-Saxons in the seventh century, vineyards are recorded as being bequeathed to abbeys and convents in many aristocratic wills, the production of sacramental wine quite possibly being their main purpose. Vineyards, although not wine production, were recorded in 731 when the Venerable Bede wrote in his *Ecclesiastical History* that "vines are cultivated in several localities".

Monastic winemaking expanded further after the Norman

Conquest in 1066, by which time grapevines were being grown in the grounds of monasteries across England, particularly in the south of the country. French monks were skilled winemakers that came to England with William the Conqueror and his nobles, who expected to drink wine with their meals. *The Domesday Book* lists some 40 vineyards, spread across southern England from East Anglia to Somerset. Leeds Castle in Kent is listed in *Domesday* as having a vineyard, as it still does today. But most of the wine preferred by the French-speaking landowning and mercantile classes was imported, and when Henry Plantagenet – whose dynastic empire included the whole of South-West France – toppled the Normans in 1154, the whole of the English market was opened up to Angevin and Bordelaise mass-producers. If they didn't kill off the English industry they certainly stopped its further development in its tracks.

From the mid-13th century, cooler summers affected grape ripening, and in the mid-14th century the Black Death created such a desperate labour shortage that grape growing almost came to a halt. Henry VIII, who came to the throne in 1509, knocked the final nails into the coffin of English winemaking: at his accession there were still 139 vineyards clinging on in abbey gardens across England and Wales; the Dissolution of the Monasteries in the late 1530s put paid to the lot of them and the Little Ice Age of the 17th century saw to it that they wouldn't be easily resurrected.

The 125 years of hostility and, more or less, endemic warfare between England and France that followed the Glorious Revolution of 1688 saw the sweet fortified wines of Spain and Portugal succeed French wines in the esteem of the English well-off. These wines were popular because they survived the long sea journeys well, presumably because they were less likely to oxidise than unfortified wines. Nevertheless, there is evidence in the 17th, 18th and 19th centuries that some noblemen in England were still growing grapes and producing wine. James I (1603–1625) had a vineyard at Weybridge, Surrey. In 1666 the gardener to Charles II, John Rose, planted vines at St James's Palace, and wrote a treatise on their cultivation, *The English Vineyard Vindicated,* advising on site selection, grape varieties, pruning, training and grapevine upkeep. Up to 2,000 vines were planted by the Earl of Salisbury, Robert Cecil, and then in 1738 the Hon. Charles Hamilton planted vines in his garden at Painshill Park, Surrey, where there is still a vineyard today. In more modern times, the Marquis of Bute planted a commercial-scale vineyard at Castell Coch, South Wales, and by the time he died in 1905 it consisted of 63,000 vines. The enthusiastic industrialist even sent his head gardener, Andrew Pettigrew, to France to learn about viticulture. Records show that the last respectable wines were produced there in 1911, and all winemaking stopped after the World War I.

Well, that's not strictly true. A very great deal of wine was made all over Britain, but not from home-grown grapes. Companies like Vine Products imported great quantities of concentrated grape must from the hotter countries of the Empire, mainly Australia and South Africa, to rehydrate and ferment here at home. Fortified British wines – termed 'British sherry' until, acting on a complaint from the Spanish, Europe banned its use – such as QC, Armadillo (sold on draught from brown plastic barrels by independent off-licences and now defunct) and supermarket own-label ranges are not only still with us but have been selling more and more strongly since the financial crisis of 2008. Wines made of imported grape concentrate are the foundation of Crabbies and Stone's ginger wines and the tonic wines Buckfast and Sanatogen. There is also a history of lower-alcohol from-concentrate table wines such as Rougemont Castle, Concorde and Silver Bay Point of 6–8% ABV. It has become the norm to describe wines made here from imported concentrate as 'British wine' while wines made from grapes actually grown here for the purpose are commonly called English, Welsh or, rather clumsily, UK wine.

If, after World War I, almost no commercial wine was made from home-grown grapes, there were vines aplenty growing in private gardens and especially in the greenhouses of the well-off, amongst whom there was a great fashion for growing exotic table fruits. George Ordish, though, was more interested in fruit for the press than for the table. In 1938 he planted vines in Wessex and the South of England, and on his travels between Kent and the Champagne region he recognised the similarity of the growing conditions. He was a talented winemaker, and his experiments in the vineyard showed that grapes could ripen in our climate. In 1953 he wrote the influential *Wine Growing in England*. Before his death in the early 1990s, Ordish had worked with another pioneer, Ray Barrington Brock, a chemist who established a research station in Oxted, Surrey, and over 25 years investigated 600 grape varieties with the aim of finding which might suit the UK. Brock acquired cuttings and vines from universities and research institutes in Europe, Russia and the United States and brought Müller-Thurgau (then called Riesling Sylvaner) and Seyvel Villard 5/276 (Seyval Blanc) to the UK. He also built a winery where he carried out experimental winemaking using different yeasts and production techniques. Brock lived until 1999 to see the start of the surge in UK grape growing, and died aged 91.

Another influence on English grape growing was the horticultural writer and broadcaster Edward Hyams who planted his own vineyard and wrote *The Grape Vine in England* and *Vineyards in England* about the history and practice of grapevine growing in England. Like Ordish, he worked with Brock and also scoured England for old grape varieties – indeed, it was he who found the Wrotham Pinot.

In 1950 an article appeared in the *Daily Mirror* called 'A bottle of Maidstone 49', which praised the work of Brock and Hyams and ended with the words "perhaps ten years hence you'll be raising a glass of sparkling Canterbury in honour of the men who made an English wine industry possible". (Some of Brock's sparkling wines were still in the cellar in his research station in the 1980s.) The prophesy was soon fulfilled when, in 1951, Major General Sir Guy Salisbury-Jones planted a commercial vineyard at Hambledon, Hampshire, and made the first English wine to be sold commercially since the First World War.

The year after that John Edginton planted his first experimental wine varieties at Lackham College in Lacock, Wiltshire. For the next decade he worked on training and pruning systems as well as new hybrid varieties, some of which made palatable wine. By 1962 he had an experimental vineyard of half an acre of new hybrid varieties of Müller, Reichensteiner and Seyval grapes. The vineyard at Teffont, Wiltshire, still operates to this day as Teffont Wines, although Mr Edginton retired in 2011.

Two more vineyards were planted in the mid-1950s: Beaulieu Estate in Hampshire and the Merrydown Wine Company in Sussex. It was a slow start, but things soon gathered pace and by the early 1990s there were more than 400 vineyards in England. Most of them were small, some being less than an acre and ranging up to five acres. Those early English winemakers tried to emulate the sweet German whites so popular at the time such as Liebfraumilch and Hock, because unlike George Ordish they regarded the English climate and growing conditions to resemble most closely those of the Rhine. There was also a uniquely English concoction known as cream wine, made by blending white and sweet red.

The first English producers to risk following Ordish's observations and make small volumes of bottled-fermented sparkling wine – but still using the Rhine-derived Müller-Thurgau and Seyval Blanc – were Nigel Godden at Pilton Manor, Somerset, who planted his vines in 1966, and Graham Barrett at Felsted, Essex, who planted his in 1967. In 1970 Sir Guy Salisbury-Jones went a step further and planted 1,000 Chardonnay vines to test bottle-fermented sparkling wine production. Salisbury-Jones also grew easier varieties such as Pinot Auxerrois and Pinot Meunier, which were used as the sparkling base wine. Unfortunately high manufacturing costs combined with the extended maturation time required meant its production was not financially viable, so production was halted.

Only in the 1980s did the industry as a whole follow Ordish's lead and start concentrating on Champagne-style sparkling wines. In 1987 Carr Taylor of Hastings, East Sussex, successfully released a bottle-fermented sparkling wine, inspiring other vineyards to follow suit but turn to more suitable varieties than the hitherto-favoured German hybrids. In 1988 Lamberhurst Vineyards of Kent went into sparkling wine production using Chardonnay, Pinot Blanc and Pinot Auxerrois all grown at New Hall Vineyards, Essex. In 1989 Rock Lodge of East Sussex made a sparkling wine called Rock Lodge Impresario. The movement grew gradually throughout the 1980s and 90s thanks to the work of pioneers such as Biddenden, Nyetimber, Chapel Down, High Weald, Camel Valley, Ridgeview and others, and by the end of the century English sparkling wines were winning gold and silver medals in competitions around the world, often trouncing competition from the stateliest of old-established Champagne houses. At a European sparkling wine competition in 2004, most of the top ten positions were taken by English wines, with French Champagnes taking the other places. English still wines have also started to win awards at major wine competitions, such as Decanter and the IWSC, and the industry is not short of innovators such as Bolney Estate with sparkling red wine, Eglantine Vineyard with dessert wine and Strawberry Hill with port-style fortified wine.

As a result of these high-profile successes, the number of vineyards and the acreage under vines has grown sharply in recent years. In 2015 there were 502 registered commercial vineyards of 0.2ha or more, of which 133 actually have wineries, and 87 registered hobby vineyards of less than 0.2ha. Currently only one per cent of the wine consumed in the UK is produced in the UK, but as both domestic production and English wine's reputation for quality grow, there is good reason to hope that more and more customers – both trade buyers and consumers – will turn to them. In 2016 alone, there were 64 new wine businesses according to HM Revenue and Customs, an increase of 73 per cent on 2015.

At the time of writing the UK is going through the process of leaving the EU and the effect this will have on UK vineyards is not yet known in detail. WineGB in April 2018 issued a press release as to its position and this can be found at **www.winegb.co.uk/industry/winegb-**

response-to-government-consultations/sition-final-30-dec-2016-BL. pdf

Some farms are planting vineyards to sell grapes to wineries, garden vineyards are growing in popularity and UK wines are becoming internationally recognised. This book is intended as a guide for all those thinking of or planning on setting up a vineyard or winery in the UK, and hopes to present them with all the issues that need to be considered.

Chapter One

Home winemaking and formal training

Maybe it's all those Mediterranean holidays, maybe it's the introduction of hardier varieties, maybe it's a sign of climate change, but a south-facing pergola smothered in the dense pale-green foliage of healthy grapevines is an increasingly common sight in Britain's back gardens. And while many of the vines you can buy in garden centres produce table fruit unsuitable for winemaking, it's perfectly possible to buy, plant, nurture and harvest grapes that, with a little care and skill, you can turn into a more than passable glass of wine.

What many grape-growing gardeners probably don't realise is that if they let themselves get carried away and plant more than 0.1ha or a quarter of an acre or 1,210 square yards with vines, their gardens become classified as 'hobby vineyards' and have to be listed as such on the UK Vineyard Register, which is kept by the Wine Standards branch of the Food Standards Agency. This is the result of Wine Regulations 2011, under which the UK was formally recognised as a wine-producing nation and which oblige the government to provide the European Commission with accurate figures regarding acreage under vines and the amount of wine the country produced.

There's no charge for registering as a hobby vineyard, and the only information you have to supply is the size of your vineyard and the number and variety of vines planted. (There is, though, a fine if you don't register within six months of planting.) As a hobby wine-maker you can enjoy or give away your wine without becoming liable for duty – but you can't sell it. However, your status changes if you plant more than half an acre or 0.2ha with vines. At that point you're no longer considered a hobbyist and any wine you make becomes liable for duty and all the other constraints and regulations you will find detailed in this book – even if you don't actually sell it.

To register your garden as a vineyard and join the existing 87 hobby vineyards, contact your local Wine Standards Officer via the Food Standards Agency website or visit **www.food. gov.uk/business-guidance/uk-vineyard-register**. For details regarding UK wine schemes and varietal regulations of the English

Wine – Protected Designation of Origin (PDO) and English Regional Wine – Protected Geographical Indication (PGI) schemes for England and Wales visit the WineGB website: **www.winegb.co.uk**. The DEFRA website also has full details of wine schemes, including permitted grape varieties for PDO and PGI wines: **www.gov.uk/guidance/eu-protected-food-names-how-to-register-food-or-drink-products**. Further details regarding UK winemaking regulations can be found in Chapter Four.

The garden vineyard

You don't need an awful lot of space to plant a few vines: they can be trained by judicious pruning to grow flat against any south-facing garden fences, walls, arches, pergolas or trellises. But they do need deep, free-draining soil; they should ideally be no more than 100m above sea level; they should be sheltered from the wind as much as possible and planted where they can get plenty of sunlight to ripen the grapes properly. The vines should be sited well away from other fruit or vegetables that could harbour pests, such as lettuces that attract light brown apple moths, and the soil's nutrient status should be checked before planting. Phosphate levels are particularly important for root growth and any additions required such as fertiliser, compost or manure should be made before planting. The level of phosphorus in the soil should be 50ppm, potassium 200ppm and magnesium 110ppm; and the potassium to magnesium ratio (K:Mg) should be 2:1 while the pH of soil should be 6.5.

Nutrient-deficient soils can take three years to correct, so before you splash out on vines and supports buy a home soil-testing kit, reagents included, from a garden centre or nursery, to test pH, nitrogen (N), phosphorus (P) and potassium (K). If you plan to plant grapevines in more than one part of the garden then all the sites should be tested, as the pH can vary wildly from one patch of soil to another. Some home grape growers may not think it's important to test the soil nutrients before planting grapevines because the back garden is already successfully growing so many other plants, and that

3

may be true if all you're planning is a few vines principally for their decorative qualities. But if what you're after is a crop that will make some quality wines, the right balance of nutrients for vine establishment, growth and yield is essential.

Grapevine suppliers can be found on the website **www.winegb. co.uk**, but before buying online you really need to be fully informed about clone and rootstock combinations and their suitability for UK soils and weather, for which see Chapter Two. Local vineyards with similar soils and WineGB members will be similarly helpful (a contact email list is available if you join the association).

Many books and websites regarding home grape growing and winemaking list varieties suitable for indoor and outdoor growth, but ultimately your choice of variety depends on local climate, soil and the style of wine you want to make. Our advice is to grow recommended wine varieties that are already thriving in the UK. It is also useful to gain vineyard knowledge and hands-on experience prior to planting grapevines in your garden (see 'Formal training' page 14) or making any type of investment. Local vineyards are a good place to volunteer for seasonal work to gain practical experience, and educational courses are available at Plumpton College in East Sussex.

There is no rule stating that garden grapevines should be planted using rootstocks instead of on their own roots or from cuttings, but planting on resistant rootstock is advisable in order to reduce the risk of phylloxera. This is a mite-borne disease native to North America that devastated vineyards across Europe in the 19th century, but American vines are partly resistant, so it's advisable to plant European Vitis vinifera varieties that are grafted on to American rootstocks. To reduce disease in general, choose a grapevine that has been proven to be successful in the UK and that suits our climate, ripens early, and doesn't suffer from bunch compaction.

How to plant grapevines in your garden

There are many ways of training grapevines in the garden, but if your aim is to produce the best quality grapes for winemaking it is advisable to use the training systems found in commercial vineyards, such as the Guyot system or the Vertical Shoot Positioned system (VSP). Techniques such as Mosel Hertz may be more aesthetically pleasing but take more work to make sure the fruit remains exposed to the sunlight during the growing season. Some training systems take more work than others, and the pruning style to be carried out will depend upon the techniques used.

The best time to plant grapevines is early spring, and they can be planted to grow up against a wall, a trellis or a fence. The vines should be spaced approximately 1.2m–1.5m apart, and the hole they are planted in should be 15cm deep and 15cm away from the wall or fence. Once it is planted, ensure the grapevine is secure it by firming the soil all around it, mulch it with compost or manure to shield the roots from frost and use tree guards to stop rabbits eating the new shoots. Let three stems grow vertically in the first year by removing any shoots growing from the side, and let the grapevines get well established before harvesting the grapes. Usually the rule is that the fruit can be harvested in the third year after planting.

Growing grapes on a garden fence

A vine trained against a fence needs the support of three or four support wires. The wires need to be galvanized and should be threaded through eyebolts securely drilled into the fence posts. The wires should be bent back and twisted to hold them in place, but not too tightly as you will probably need to adjust the tension at different times during the growing season.

Growing garden grapes in containers

Vines can also be planted in large pots. A heavy-based clay container will retain its stability as the vine grows – and remember that the vine can remain in its pot for several years. Potted grapevines need to have the top 15cm of compost removed every spring and a new layer added. They also need regular watering and foliar feeding during the growing season. Grapevines grown in pots are often spur-pruned and can be trained to one stem tied to a bamboo cane with five or six branches at the top. In the first year of growth, remove all grapes and unwanted lateral shoots from the grapevine. The stems that grow around the base should also be removed.

Management of fence-grown grapevines

Pruning grapevines that grow against a wall or fence can be a confusing business, but it's important to get it right. Correct pruning will sustain the vine's ability to produce a good-quality crop by improving grapevine structure, exposing bunches to sunlight, encouraging the growth of next year's canes and helping to curb the incidence of disease and pests by improving the circulation of air.

The most important part of pruning is selecting the good-quality fruiting wood that must be retained on the grapevine and will hold the grape bunches. Only minimal pruning of one-year-old shoots is needed, but selected trimming may be required to train the shape of the vine before the second year's growth starts. All lateral shoots and all fruit that grows on the trunk should be snipped off. The permanent structure is the cordon on the top wire. During January and February (although some UK vineyards start pruning in December), each one-year-old shoot on the cordon should be pruned to either a three- or four-node spur (fruit spur) or a one-node renewal spur (vegetative spur). The spurs to be used as fruiting spurs should have the diameter of a pencil. The vegetative spur produces the shoots that will be the following year's fruit spurs.

Keep the vines free from weeds either by hand weeding or mulching. Spring frost can damage the trunks of young grapevines or even kill them completely. There are several ways to prevent frost damage, but if you only have a few vines try using straw mulch around the base of each vine and covering the plant with plastic – both can be removed when the weather improves.

Pests and diseases

While the UK is largely phylloxera-free nowadays, there are many other pests and diseases that will menace your grapevines, especially the bunch rot or grey mould produced by *Botrytis cinerea*, powdery mildew (*Oidium tuckeri*) and to a lesser extent downy mildew (*Perono-*

Case study
Simpsons Vineyard, Kent
www.simpsonswine.com

Simpson's vineyard was started by Charles and Ruth Simpson in 2014, after having moved back from France where they also operate a vineyard in the Languedoc region.

The size and quality of the 2018 harvest is record breaking and Charles and Ruth have had a bumper harvest. "We harvested 30 tonnes of grapes, producing 20,000 bottles, in 2016. In 2017, we lost 60 per cent of our crop to frost meaning that we took in around the same volume as the previous year," said Charles Simpson. "We're expecting 200 tonnes this year and that changes everything," At the moment they produce a still Chardonnay, but there are plans to produce a sparkling wine, a Provençal style rosé and a still red Pinot Noir.

Although the English vineyard industry is doing extremely well at the moment, there are production problems because although there are a large number of vineyards, there are not enough wineries and therefore not enough capacity. Simpsons operate a winery but they have had to bring in additional tanks from France, with four x 10,000 litre capacity reaching the vineyard just before harvest started.

With the ever importance of visitors to the vineyard to boost trade, Simpsons has become part of Wine Garden of England **www.winegardenofengland.co.uk**. This is an organisation set up in Kent to promote Kent's wine producers. Also included are vineyards, Biddenden, Domaine Evremond, Chapel Down, Gusbourne, Hush Heath and Squerryes. Wine Garden of England have organised a wine festival at Rochester Cathedral in November.

The Simpsons are optimistic of expanding into overseas markets and are already in discussions with distributors in both United States and Denmark. However with the ever nearing Brexit looming, Ruth is very concerned about the future with regards employing mainly Eastern European pickers. Twice as many pickers will be required in 2019, which could become a difficult problem to resolve.

spora viticola). A preventive measure is to spray seaweed extract every two weeks during the growing season (except around flowering) to strengthen the vine's foliage. Wettable sulfur and Dithane or Mancozeb help to protect the vines against mildews. The 'Bordeaux blend' of sulfur and copper has been used for many years, but it is important never to spray when flowering to ensure there is no disruption to pollination and fertilisation. Spray application times and recommended concentration rates must be strictly adhered to in order to prevent damage to the growth of the grapevines. Sprays can be bought from specialist suppliers.

Other diseases to be aware of include phomopsis cane and leaf spot, and the grapevine trunk disease *Botryosphaeria*, particularly the Diplodia seriata species (prev. *Botryosphaeria obtusa*). This particular species is the most widespread of all trunk fungi in vines and other plants, but is relatively nonthreatening compared to some others. Another to look out for is blackfoot disease (caused by *Cylindrocarpon fungus*). Chemical sprays are used in many wine regions throughout the world, and some are certified for use in organic viticulture.

Common vineyard pests in the UK include rabbits, deer, badgers, spider mites, beetles, grape berry moths, thrips, erineum mites, wasps, birds and vine weevils. Some pests, like deer, will not affect the garden grape grower as much as commercial grape growers, but protecting grapes from birds and wasp damage in the summer is of utmost importance. Identification of the disease or pest is paramount; learning about their life cycle and monitoring them will enable an informed decision regarding biological, cultural and chemical control options.

Buying grapes for home winemaking

A large and well-established hobby vineyard will yield enough grapes to be worth selling, perhaps under contract to a local winery. Top quality in-demand sparkling wine varieties can command £2,000 a tonne at time of writing, although obviously prices fluctuate enormously from vintage to vintage. Bacchus commands slightly less at between £1,600–£1,800 per tonne. Other varieties such as Reichensteiner, Seyval Blanc, Ortega command around £1,500 per tonne. Having said this, prices fluctuate significantly from year to year on the open market. In years of high demand (e.g. 2016, 2017) where supply is limited due to weather factors such as frost or poor flowering, the prices paid for sparkling varieties can rise to £3,500 per tonne. This is exceptional and must never be expected or assumed in a business plan.

It should be assumed by new industry entrants that as the supply of grapes increases, then prices paid for grapes will come down. Assume that prices for sparkling varieties will come down to £1,600 –£1,800 per tonne over the next five years.

A mature, well-sited and well-managed half-acre vineyard might produce two tonnes in a good year. However, you'll probably want to use your fruit for your own winemaking. If you have a large enough harvest, you can have the job professionally done by a contract winery, or – cheaper, useful practice for the future and infinitely more fun – you can do it yourself.

While your own grapevines are becoming established it may be useful to contact a local vineyard or winery to buy a few bunches for your first homemade wine. Some vineyards may prefer to sell larger quantities but others may be happy to sell smaller amounts or may know someone who has grapes to sell.

Home winemaking kits and equipment

You can buy simple home winemaking kits either at a local homebrew shop or online for very little money with all the equipment, ingredients (including grape juice concentrate) and process aids you need in order to teach yourself the principles and basic practicalities. There are also dozens of books of recipes and instructions on the market to aid and direct your early experimentations.

There will soon come a time, though, when you want to scale up and the old homebrew kit is no longer adequate. And as the differences between the professional and the amateur are not merely a matter of scale but also of the degree of control the professional must exert, you might as well start with a full suite of laboratory apparatus. The most important item is the hydrometer in its calibrated flask, which measures the density – i.e. the sugar content – of the juice and enables you to monitor both the grape ripening pre-harvest and the progress of your fermentation. Along with the hydrometer you'll need a good thermometer since the density of the juice depends not only on its sugar level but also on the temperature. Acidity is also important, so you'll need a pH meter – litmus paper to start with, but more sophisticated titration equipment later on to measure not only acidity but also sulfur dioxide levels.

For home winemaking on any sort of scale you can buy a small crusher/destemming machine to speed up the business of extracting the juice from the fruit. Your starter kit will include a 10L bucket with lid to contain the first fermentation and a 4.5L plastic or glass demijohn with bored bung, bubbler airlock and siphon for the slow secondary fermentation. You will soon want to trade up to much larger fermenters with taps to avoid all the mess of siphoning. Straining bags for racking, plastic jugs, funnels and spare buckets are all essential as is a plentiful supply of sodium or potassium metabisulfite, either in powder form or as 5mg Campden tablets, which is used both to sterilise all your equipment and to kill bacteria and wild yeast in the juice and prevent oxidation of the wine. Bottling equipment including six bottles, corks, corking machine, shrink caps and labels may also be required for the finished wine.

The **www.lovebrewing.co.uk** website is a good starting point. Other informative sites are:
www.homewinemaking.co.uk, **www.hopshopuk.com**
www.hopandgrape.co.uk, **www.homebrewshop.co.uk**
www.homebrewit.co.uk, **www.art-of-brewing.co.uk**
www.brewgenie.co.uk, **www.the-online-homebrew-company.co.uk**
www.beaverdalewinekits.co.uk, **www.goodlifehomebrew.com**
www.creativewinemaking.co.uk and **www.vigoltd.com**

Case study
Fred Langdale, Vineyard manager
www.extonparkvineyard.com

Fred Langdale only took a labouring job back in 2001 to help pay for his youthful globe-trotting. But the job – leaf-thinning, green-harvesting, and netting – was in a vineyard; and not just any vineyard either, but the prestigious Peregrine Wines Vineyard in the Gibbston Valley in Central Otago, New Zealand.

The experience ignited an interest in viticulture, and on returning to the UK in 2003 he enrolled on the two-day-a-week Principles of Vine-growing course at Plumpton College in Sussex. The other three days he worked at the organic Davenport Vineyard nearby, both in the vineyard and in the winery, where he was a willing bottling, labelling, and cleaning dogsbody.

That Plumpton College course may only have been part-time, but combined with Fred's practical experience at Peregrine and Davenport it was enough to land him a year's work at L'Avenir in Stellenbosch, South Africa, supervising a harvest team of 60 and completing the winter pruning, and proving a solid foundation for a stellar career in viticulture. From 2006-2008 Fred supervised the creation a new 32ha plot for Nyetimber in West Sussex; and then in 2008 he became vineyard manager at what was then a fairly new (first planted 2003) sparkling wine producer, Exton Park Vineyard in Hampshire.

Since then Fred has seen Exton Park change ownership and has played a key role in its expansion to become one of England's most productive sparkling wine producers, doubling the area under cultivation from its original 12ha and helping with the addition of a brand-new state-of-the-art winery under the supervision of top French winemaker Corinne Seeley. He has been instrumental in developing the 55 acre Exton Park vineyard as it is today.

Home winemaking preparation

There are many winemaking recipes available for home winemaking as well as 'ready to use' winemaking kits available from suppliers. Presented in this chapter is a modified method of the small-scale red wine vinification commonly used in wine research trials. This can be carried out using different sized fermentation vessels – 4.5L, 10L or 30L, according to the quantity of fruit you have. The steps are the same.

You'll need 6–7kg of grapes to produce 5L of wine; if you don't have quite enough you can always top it up with concentrate. Hygiene is absolutely critical, so sterilise all your equipment even before you pick your grapes. Methods vary, but a good scrub down with mild bleach or Milton Fluid wipes (unperfumed, of course!) followed by a thorough rinse in scalding hot water and then a good swill round with a sulfur dioxide/citric acid-based sanitiser (available from home winemaking shops) should kill any lurking bugs. Avoid chlorine, soap, detergent or anything perfumed as they are difficult to wash off completely and can affect the taste of your finished wine. Wear gloves when using and preparing sanitising solutions as they are caustic and can cause irritation.

Home red winemaking recipe

Here's a basic red winemaking technique for the home winemaker; further recipes for home white winemaking and fruit winemaking can be found at **www.lovebrewing.co.uk**.

The specific gravity on the hydrometer needs to be between 1078 and 1090, depending on the alcohol level you are aiming for. A reading of 1090 will normally produce a wine of 13% ABV while 1078 will result in 11.5% ABV. This can be adjusted by adding grape concentrate or cane sugar prior to fermentation: the Wine Standards branch figure of 16.5g of sugar per litre of juice to produce 1% ABV is slightly low. Germany authorities give 16.85g/l, Australians say 16.95g/l and France suggests 17g/l. The legal limit for alcohol increase in wine is 3 per cent.

The grape bunches should be de-stemmed and crushed and only the juice, skins and pips should go into the fermenter. Small quantities of destemmed fruit can be crushed by hand, or you might use a food processor with a tight lid. Larger quantities can be ground to pulp in a bucket using a piece of wood. Don't fill the fermenter to the top or the carbon dioxide produced by the yeast will cause it to overflow spectacularly. **Additionally, make sure the room is well ventilated as CO^2 is extremely dangerous**.

The enzyme pectinase can be added at this stage to help the juice settle: it's not required in red wine but is common in white winemaking. Make up a yeast culture according to the manufacturer's instructions, and an hour after adding the enzyme add the yeast culture and nutrients to the juice as recommended by the manufacturer. The juice should ferment at 19–27°C (lower for white wine) and should certainly never rise above 30°C. Take its temperature twice daily during fermentation; at the same time you should use a rolling pin or potato masher or other kitchen implement to break up and punch down the cap of seeds and skins that will form on top of the wine. These tannins and colours will need extracting.

You should also be measuring the gravity twice a day with a hydrometer; the primary fermentation is complete when you get a consistent hydrometer reading of 990-1000 and the cap of skin and pips has sunk to the bottom of the container. At this point siphon the free liquid into sterile demijohns, press all the remaining liquid out of the pulp or pomace and add that to the demijohns too, and add a malolactic culture (again, available from a homebrew shop or online). This will help your wine mellow and mature. Finally seal up the demijohns with bungs and airlocks and leave them in a dark place at a consistent 18°C for four to six weeks.

To make white wine, add pectinase as above and strain all the skins, seeds and any other solids from the juice before pitching it with yeast and nutrients as instructed and transferring it to demijohns to ferment, ideally at a temperature of 12–15°C. If you like your wine oaked, oak extract or oak chips can be stirred in while the wine matures. When fermentation has finished the wine will need clarifying using finings to get rid of any remaining proteins. It can also be filtered to achieve perfect clarity, although the flavour might suffer.

Formal training

Part-time and full-time courses

If you are truly passionate or have decided on winemaking as a career, home winemaking will only take you so far. There will come a point at which you will need both academic training and experience with commercial-scale equipment.

Whether you are planting a commercial vineyard or a hobby vineyard it is essential to gain an understanding of grapevine biology and its annual growth cycle and management. For in-depth practical and theory-based training in viticulture and oenology it is advisable to attend a specialised course. There are limited training options available in the UK, but there are viticulture and oenology undergraduate degrees available in Europe (although they are not taught in English). Some universities in Europe offer viticulture and oenology postgraduate degrees taught in English, but there are cost implications to consider. International viticulture and oenology training and degrees are taught in English in Canada, the United States, Australia, South Africa and New Zealand, but these have tuition fees, relocation expenses and visa requirements to consider.

The Wine and Spirits Education Trust **www.wset.co.uk** provides training for those who wish to enter or are currently working in the wine trade. Qualification levels and modules are based on the needs of wine trade and business employees, and include basic viticulture and oenology modules.

The Institute of the Master of Wines **www.mastersofwine.org** qualification is the wine industry's highest qualification and the Institute recommends that applicants hold the WSET Diploma, or another wine qualification of at least the same level (a bachelor or master's degree in oenology). Applicants must also have at least five years' professional experience in the industry.

Founded in 1926, Plumpton College offers a wide selection of programmes in land-based subjects to over 3,000 students a year, and is the UK's international centre for wine education, training and research. In association with the Royal Agricultural University, the

Case study
Sarah Midgley, Winemaker at Plumpton College
www.plumpton.ac.uk

Formal degree-level training in the various aspects of oenology is a great launchpad for a career as a winemaker - but failing that, while studying for her BSc, Sarah Midgley developed an interest in wine and that led to her spending some years criss-crossing the Pacific.

Her first wine qualification was a WSET Level 2, which she achieved while working in a pub that specialised in wines from around the world. She then took up a place on the one-year intensive Postgraduate Diploma in Viticulture and Oenology at Lincoln University, New Zealand.

Sarah gained her practical experience from working abroad and did summer contract vineyard work at Premium Viticulture, Marlborough, New Zealand in 2008. Sarah's first paid harvest was in 2009 at Tyrrell's Glenbawn Winery, Australia.

In 2009 Sarah worked at William's Selyem Winery, California, for her second vintage and found it extremely useful from a formal training perspective. They dedicate several days at the start of harvest to training and safety briefings for their staff. In 2010 she worked at Kim Crawford Wines in Marlborough, New Zealand, operating and cleaning the nine presses, the crusher/destemmer, quality control and directing the flow of the juice from press to tanks. Further winemaking experience was gained at Tyrrell's Winery, Pokolbin, Hunter Valley, Australia in 2011. Due to a fairly small harvest from a difficult growing season, Sarah found she had less work than expected but was invited to help in the winery and laboratory at Cassegrain Wines, Port Macquarie, NSW, Australia.

All this time Sarah had also been taking advantage of the seasonal difference between the northern and southern hemispheres to spend the rest of the year including British autumn as assistant winemaker at Cornwall's Camel Valley Vineyards. The opportunities for career development offered by working two harvests a year paid off handsomely in Autumn 2014 when Sarah was appointed winemaker at Plumpton College.

wine division offers graduate and master's degrees in wine business and production to around 150 students. It also delivers industry training all over the UK through its WineSkills scheme www.wineskills.co.uk; Plumpton has been a key factor in the successful development of the English and Welsh wine industry. The College manages a commercial vineyard that produces award-winning wine, and participates in research projects with universities in France, Germany, Italy, Romania and Australia. www.plumpton.ac.uk or email Enquiries@plumpton.ac.uk.
Tel: +44 (0)1273 890454.
For specific wine enquiries contact, Chris Foss, Curriculum Manager for the Wine Division.
email chris.foss@plumpton.ac.uk. Tel: + 44 (0)1273 892018.

Work experience at home and abroad

Most of the international viticulture and oenology two and three year courses include a work placement or vintage experience module. There are several vineyard and winery employment recruitment websites where international jobs are advertised. www.winejobs online.com is New Zealand-based but often has jobs advertised around the world. The Australian vineyard and winery recruitment site www.wineindustryjobs.com.au and www.vitijob.com both advertise international vacancies. Additionally www.winebusiness.com advertises industry roles in the USA. Many vineyards advertise employment opportunities on their websites and require application direct to the company. However you will require an Employment Authorization Document.

International vineyards and wineries often prefer applicants to have qualifications or previous experience, but enthusiastic students and individuals are often welcome. For European countries it is advised to contact them in their own language as it is more likely that you will receive a response, and you may need to speak the language of the country to work in some wineries. Applying direct to UK vineyards and wineries or via the WineGB for either paid or voluntary work can be successful at the right time of year, such as prior to pruning or before summer canopy management work begins. Recently there has been an increase in wineries and vineyards using social media, and some employment vacancies are advertised on Facebook groups such as 'Travelling Winemakers – Living the dream!!' or 'The Cellarhand' at **www.facebook.com**.

Another very useful source if looking for work both in the UK and overseas is **www.finevintageltd.com**. They run the following websites:

WineJobsCanada.com
WineJobsUSA.com
WineJobsCalifornia.com
WineJobsAustralia.com
WineJobsChina.com
WineJobsEngland.co.uk
WineJobsHongKong.com
WineJobsIreland.com
WineJobsNewZealand.com
WineJobsScandinavia.com
WineJobsScotland.co.uk
WineJobsSingapore.com
EmpleosVinoEspana.com
EmpregosVinhosPortugal.com
EmpleosVinoSudamerica.com

In addition they run WSET courses in USA, Canada and Italy and also provide wine tours to Bordeaux, Champagne-Burgundy, Napa, Tuscany and Spain.

Visa requirements, costs and the official paper work should be completed several months in advance because some visas require police and medical checks. Transport and travel to an overseas winery is not paid for by the employer, and neither are visa costs.

The Craft Distillers' Handbook

A practical guide to the making and marketing of spirits

Ted Bruning

"This is a brilliant book for those seeking to know what running a distillery entails and how to get started"

Alex Davies, Head Distiller, Kyoto Distillery, Japan

The Craft Distillers' Handbook

A practical guide to the making and marketing of spirits

"I built one of the first small distilleries in the UK and found the information in this book invaluable"
Tony Reeman-Clark, Strathearn Distillery

Ted Bruning

- Microdistilling has never been more popular. The number of gin distilleries alone, opening in the UK in 2017, was 45 with gin sales now reaching £1 billion
- A very practical guide with 10 case studies of those who have started their own distilleries
- Get inside information on developing the necessary skills, calculating the finances and finding the right premises
- Find out what equipment you'll need, where to get it – and how much you would pay!
- Formulate and market your own brand of top-quality spirits and liqueurs
- **£10.95 plus postage and packing**

www.posthousepublishing.com

Chapter Two

Land and soil

U K commercial vineyards are divided into the 370 that don't have winemaking facilities and the 133 that do. Most vineyards are situated in the South West (Cornwall, Devon, Dorset, Somerset, Gloucestershire) and South East (Hampshire, Surrey, Kent, Sussex and Wiltshire) of England, with others in East Anglia and the Midlands, and some further north and in Wales. There has been a change in grape varieties in recent years, with an increase in the classic sparkling wine varieties, Chardonnay, Pinot Noir and Pinot Meunier, although the still wines made from other varieties, such as Pinot Gris, Pinot Noir and Bacchus, have always been well received.

Annual production fluctuates tremendously in the UK depending on the weather during the growing season. The total harvest in 2015 was 38,000 hectolitres, with the largest recorded so far in 2014 at 48,267 and other large harvests occurred in 2006, 1996 and 1992. However, 2012 was a wash-out. More statistical information can be found on the Food Standards Agency website: **www.food.gov.uk/ business-industry/winestandards/ukvineyards**.

When thinking about becoming a vineyard owner, the most important consideration is the target market for the wines. Investigate your target market and whether it is realistic for your wine style/product and how your wine will be marketed to that sector. This information will not only form the core of your business plan, it will also determine your vineyard design details such as grape variety, training system and canopy management techniques.

Buying an existing vineyard

Specialist land agents such as Savills **www.savills.co.uk**, Strutt&Parker **www.struttandparker.com**, Knight Frank **www.knightfrank.co.uk**, Turner Butler **www.turnerbutler.co.uk** and Carter Jonas **www.carterjonas.co.uk**, and dedicated websites such as **www.uklandandfarms. co.uk**, occasionally advertise vineyards for sale as well as land suitable for vineyards. The WineGB members' email list also sometimes carries details of vineyards for sale.

There are advantages and disadvantages to buying an existing vineyard. While the hard work of soil preparation, trellising and planting has already been done, the purchaser inherits the vendor's choice of varieties and method of training, and if they're not suitable for the wine style the new owners want to produce, then the whole vineyard will need re-planting. The purchaser also inherits the reputation of the previous owner's wines and the experience and expertise of the workforce. This is great if the wine already has a reputation for quality, but can be challenging if the vendor lacked expertise and the buyer has to improve standards in the vineyard and winery at the same time as managing the business and its staff as well as driving sales.

Once the purchaser is satisfied on that score, thorough background research into the business, its sales and marketing strategy, existing planning permissions, space for expansion and what is included in the sale (such as the library wine stock) is essential. The prospective buyer absolutely must have full access to the vineyard's audited accounts and its existing stockists and markets. There ought to be plenty of buildings on site, both as secure storage for expensive capital equipment such as tractors and sprayers and because it gives the buyer a better chance of getting planning permission for a new winery or the expansion of an existing one. It's also very useful if there's already a house on site: harvest time means early starts!

Sometimes existing vineyards are not as expensive as you might believe. For example a single hectare in Combe Hay near Bath, which included a vineyard of about a quarter of a hectare (enough to deliver 1,000 bottles a year), sold prior to auction off a guide price of £15,000. If the land had gone to auction it would probably have sold for far more, and in general a decent acreage under vines is worth twice the going rate for agricultural land, especially if it is well-located and well-tended with the correct trellis system and good clones and rootstocks. A productive, established vineyard would be placed on the market for £25,000–£35,000 per acre. There are already precedents set for this. Good vineyards planted in the last 15 years do not generally come up for sale in the UK.

Buying land to plant a vineyard

Selecting a suitable and appropriate site is without doubt the most important decision the prospective viticulturalist will ever make. Vineyard consultants and land agents are on hand to help and advise, but the final and irrevocable decision is the purchaser's to make, so never leap without a really thorough look!

The physical properties of the site you need to check – altitude, aspect, soil, drainage, frost and wind protection – are detailed in the site assessment on the following page, but there are other questions the purchaser needs to ask. Is the vineyard the right size to be both viable and manageable? Is any additional land available to allow for future expansion? You might well at some point seek to expand your operation in ways that will require permission, so now is the best time to ask questions that will be raised then, such as: is there space for ancillary buildings such as a shop and/or visitor centre? Is the road access adequate? Is there sufficient car-parking? Are there neighbours who might object to increased traffic? Could the waste disposal facilities cope with greater demand, or could they be improved? Planning matters will be dealt with in more detail in Appendix II, but it's a very good idea to liaise from the beginning with the district council's Development Control department which will be handling any application you might make. Guidance can also be sought from established vineyards that have already been through the planning process.

Once you've found a site that seems right in enough respects to be feasible, the next thing to think about is money. The whole question of finance will be looked at in Chapter Ten but as a very rough guide to land prices in the South-East in 2017, an acre of agricultural land suitable for a vineyard would be in the region of £15,000. And as vines take time to establish and develop, it is unlikely that the new owner would see any income for five to seven years in the case of sparkling wine production, possibly less for still wines. The predicted budget is around £10–12,000 per acre to plant and establish a vineyard. This includes grapevines, posts and trellis systems but not the machinery, labour costs or consultancy fees.

Site assessment

In the northern hemisphere the best vineyard sites face south for maximum sunlight throughout the growing season. It is important to investigate the climate of the site, particularly growing degree days (GDD), which is the number of days above 10°C during the growing season. This is the system that is commonly used to determine which grapes are most suitable for the location in question, but it's also important to check the lowest site temperatures for the past 10–15 years to give an indication of frost risk. If the site does not have a weather station, or the data is not readily available from the seller, then use the information from the nearest Met Office weather station.

It is important to find out what the land was previously used for, what other crops are planted nearby and if there is another vineyard in the vicinity. Some crops may encourage grapevine pests or disease, and the possibility of chemical spray drift from neighbouring properties should be considered. Study the general geography of the land, as a small very steep slope on one side could cause problems for labour, machinery and grape berry ripening. Enquire about the main local pests such as rabbits, badgers and deer, as it is important to establish whether deer fences will need to be installed. If rabbits are the main pest, fencing is not the only method of control, but you don't have to use toxic substances as there are organic options (See Chapter Three).

Slope: in the cool UK climate elevation is important as grape acidity increases as the altitude increases. A slope of above five per cent is recommended at 100m above sea level. The slope should be enough to provide drainage of cold air, which is important when spring frosts occur, and allows for water drainage. Cold air is heavier than warm air so settles on the low land, and cold air moves quicker downhill when the slope is steep. Obstacles such as trees impede the path of the cold air and should be removed as part of the site preparation prior to planting. Although successful steep slope viticulture can be found in some wine regions, specifically in the Rheingau in Germany where special equipment is being developed to carry out vineyard work, extremely steep slopes are difficult for both workers and machinery, and increase the chance of soil erosion.

Aspect: the preferred aspect of a vineyard slope in the UK, where summers are cool and GDD is low, is south-facing (south, south-east or south-west). South-facing vineyards in Europe warm earlier in the spring, and grapevines will warm more on sunny days when they are facing south than on a north-facing site. Vineyards with an east part (SE) benefit from the morning sun and dry more quickly from rain and dew than they do on a south west-facing slope, which reduces disease incidence.

Previous use: knowing what the land was used for previously will tell you whether it is compatible with the growing of grapevines. It is a good idea to list the entire past crop and/or animal use and management practices, along with past herbicide use. This is an important aspect of vineyard site selection, as considerations must be made for pesticide or fungicide residues; some agricultural sprays can stay in the soil for a long time and are toxic to new vines. In addition any soil adjustments and pest problems need to be dealt with on every part of the site. Find out if the site has ever been altered or levelled in any way; some trees and plants, especially oak trees, can leave behind rot diseases in old roots, so sites that were previously forest should lie fallow for one year (preferably three to five years) to decrease the fungal inoculum in the soil.

Soil and drainage: tests to determine soil type, texture, depth, fertility/nutrition and water-holding capacity are absolutely critical, as these factors determine how it should be treated and managed. The soil profile is determined by digging a pit and taking samples at 0–30cm and 30–100cm to test both topsoil and subsoil. Samples must be taken across the site, usually 15–20 are taken on a 12-ha site. All non-uniform areas should be tested, including hills or dips. A soil report can include organic matter, soil colour, texture, rock (amount, size and type), soil structure and particle aggregation, soil porosity and approximate moisture content, plus relevant comments such as signs of poor drainage.

Cranfield University offers a free online soil map of the UK, which breaks down to very small localised areas. It does not include nutrient analysis but does give info on soil texture, fertility and natural drainage. It is a very useful resource at **www.landis.org.uk/soilscapes**. Other commercial providers of soil analysis using gps, and offering soil maps showing nutrient variation are SOYL **www.soyl. com/services/nutrient-mapping** and Lancrop **www.lancrop.com/ content/lancrop-en.aspx**. SOYL will carry out a 'Soil Health Check' analysis. This gives a texture test, cation exchange capacity, organic matter content, macro nutrients and micro nutrients. Soil nutrient samples only need to be taken from two zones: 0–15cm and 15–30cm. Certainly dig soil pits down to 1m but only to ascertain the soil profile, depth of the individual horizons and soil texture.

Additionally Laverstoke Farm Park in Hampshire has a fully equipped comprehensive analytical chemistry laboratory for soil and food analysis: **www.laverstokepark.co.uk/about-us/we-believe/ analytical-chemistry-lab/**.

It is essential that soil analysis results are correctly interpreted so that a treatment plan can be prepared before planting. The ideal soil pH for growing grapes is a range between 6.5–7.5, although they can be grown in soils with pH of up to 8 if suitably tolerant rootstocks are used. High pH levels limit the availability of nutrients, including phosphorus, iron, manganese, boron, copper and zinc, although rootstock selection can ease the problem slightly. Soil liming before planting can also alleviate the root zone problem, but soil pH will have to be monitored through the life of the vineyard since acidity from untreated areas will eventually affect treated soil, reducing the pH.

Excessive nitrogen in the soil of a site should be avoided, or planted with a plant that will remove/compete for the excessive nitrogen. Nitrogen, potassium, phosphorus, calcium, magnesium and sulfur are macro-nutrients in soil essential for grapevine growth. Micronutrients include chlorine, iron, boron, manganese, zinc, copper and

Case study
Buying an existing vineyard — Greyfriars, Surrey
www.greyfriarsvineyard.co.uk

Mike Wagstaff first became intrigued by the potential of growing grapes and making wine in England after picking up a copy of *Winelands of Britain* by his former geology lecturer at Imperial College, Richard Selley. At the time, Mike had a full-time job running an Aberdeen-based oil company. It was not until the company was taken over in 2009 that he and his wife Hilary had the time and capital to think more seriously about owning a vineyard.

They spent six months researching the commercial viability of wine-making in England before embarking on the search for a site that would eventually lead them to Greyfriars, Puttenham, on the North Downs outside Guildford in Surrey. It was another six months before they finally took possession, and they soon found that buying an existing vineyard rather than starting from scratch had its disadvantages as well as its advantages.

On the positive side, an existing vineyard has a track record that the buyer can verify. Most of the start-up's teething troubles should have been solved; it should come with some existing vineyard and/or winery infrastructure and equipment; and it should already be trading. Greyfriars had been planted 20 years earlier, and had a history of success with Pinot Noir and Chardonnay.

On the negative side, the buyer is stuck with the previous owner's varietal and clone selection, planting and trellising system. Varieties that were fashionable 10 or 20 years ago may not work today, thanks to changes in vineyard technology and popular tastes over time. At Greyfriars, however, this wasn't a problem. Only 0.5ha had been planted (85 per cent Chardonnay, 15 per cent Pinot Noir), and there was plenty more suitable land on the site. This gave Mike the space to expand to a size that would support the necessary investment in vineyard equipment, but the opportunity to make his own decisions about planting.

At first the Wagstaffs made minimal changes to the existing vineyard in order to understand properly what they had inherited. Since they planned to make sparkling wine there was no need to change grape varieties; the 16ha of new planting since 2010 have also been Chardonnay and Pinot Noir, with the addition of some Pinot Meunier. The existing vines were in good condition despite their age, although some had to be replaced in the first two years. While they did not change the training system from Double Guyot, they had to replace all the old wooden trellising posts in the existing vineyard with steel.

Since 2011 they expanded the vineyard by planting an additional 40 acres of the three classic Champagne grape varieties: Chardonnay, Pinot Noir and Pinot Meunier. They have also completed a major redevelopment of the existing winery to accommodate the resulting increased production levels.

They have gone on to produce a Chardonnay, Still Rosé, Sparkling Rosé and a Sparkling Classic Cuvée which reflects the unique geology, soil conditions, climate and heritage of the wonderful landscape of the Surrey North Downs.

Helping Mike and Hilary achieve their dream were two highly trusted advisors: vineyard manager David Line – who studied viticulture at Plumpton College in Sussex - and German-born wine consultant Hans Schleifer who, according to Mike, knows more about wine making in England than anyone else and is, quite simply, "... worth his weight in gold."

The vineyard offers tours with wine tasting and the tour of the vineyard finishes with a tutored tasting of several of their award-winning sparkling and still wines. The tastings normally take place on the newly built viewing deck situated in the middle of one of the vineyards. The tour costs £12 per person and takes about 90 minutes. They also offer a 10 per cent discount on all wine purchased on the day of the tour.

molybdenum. Both an excess and a deficiency of these nutrients cause visible symptoms in grapevines that affect grape berry ripening and can have implications for winemaking. Phosphorus levels in soils in the UK for grapevines should be 50ppm, potassium levels should be 200ppm, magnesium 110ppm and the potassium to magnesium ratio (K:Mg) should be 2:1. Nutrient-deficient soils can take a minimum of three years to correct, and this should be factored into the site preparation before planting. Certain pest nematodes may cause problems in vineyards, and populations are typically higher in sandy soils. It is wise to have the soil tested for nematodes before site selection and planting.

Grapevines don't like wet feet because too much water limits the amount of oxygen available to the root system. Poor drainage also means that the soil takes longer to warm up in spring. It also restricts root growth, which leads to a reduction in drought resistance and mineral deficiency; it increases soil compaction; it harbours fungal diseases; and it causes berry swelling and juice dilution. To improve soil drainage before planting, ditches can be dug on the site, drainage pipe systems installed and sub-soiling carried out if required. Subsurface water can be removed using tiling, which is a system of perforated plastic pipes fitted under the vineyard. Subsoil drainage uses a plastic pipe, called a drain tile, at a recommended depth in the soil, so that surplus water flows into the drain tile to a ditch. If the vineyard site needs to have a drainage system installed prior to planting, use a qualified, experienced agricultural drainage engineer. Mole drains are another form of drainage similar to tiling but without the tile itself being installed. They are cheaper to install, but have a limited life. Soils must be at least 30 per cent clay and 40 per cent silt for the channel to remain steady for a couple of years, and have hardly any machinery traffic passing down the rows. Remember also that the water that drains off the vineyard site must comply with local water authority guidelines.

Site preparation
Soil preparation to correct the pH, nutrition, drainage, compaction level and texture will dramatically improve the chances of the

young vines' survival in the early years. Additions advised in your soil report, such as nutrient supplements including lime, must be carried out before planting. If a cover crop is required to raise soil nutrient levels in the alleyways between vine rows, they ought to be established before planting too. Shrubs and trees around the edge of the site that are not suitable for windbreaks may need to be removed to prevent shading of the grapevines, improve airflow in the vineyard and minimise pests and disease. Living windbreaks such as trees need to be installed early enough to allow them to grow before planting the vine themselves. Rocks and large stones can make it difficult or impossible to drive in the posts for training systems, so they and other unwanted debris (especially old tree-roots, see above) need to be removed too. This might well need heavy equipment that you might be able to borrow but can certainly hire. Weed can be sprayed with glyphosate; however some weeds can take longer than a year to eradicate completely. It is advisable to investigate which pests are common in the local area, i.e. rabbits, deer or badgers, and a pest management strategy considered including the erection of a deer fence if necessary.

Windbreaks

The dominant winds in the UK are the south-west winds, which causes rain but is quite mild; the easterly wind, which is dry and warm in summer but cold in winter; the southerly wind, which is hot and dry with thunderstorms; and the north-westerly winds, which are cold with rain showers and snow in winter. Wind will cool the microclimate of the grape clusters and cause damage to vines and trellis systems.

Living windbreaks compete with grapevines for soil space, water and nutrients can increase vine shading, increase frost risk and have a cost implication to plant/sustain as well as being home to birds that will be vineyard pests. But they also reduce wind damage, increase clusters per shoot by increasing fruitset and yield, produce larger leaves, increase vine productivity and reduce spray drift. It may be possible to plant several rows of windbreak trees using various species and including other fruit and nut-bearing bushes and shrubs that can themselves be harvested (see Chapter Nine).

Alternatively you can install artificial windbreaks using polyethylene netting on posts or straightforward lap, panel or featheredged garden fencing that don't have to be maintained. However, they're expensive and therefore only practical over short runs, and of course they do degrade over time.

Grape varieties

This is the moment of truth and what all the effort and expense has been about – the grape varieties you're going to plant. In the early days English winegrowers believed their soil and climate were most similar to those of Germany, a belief reflected in their choice of variety – mostly Müller-Thugau and a selection of particularly resilient German-based hybrids. It was soon realised that the South-East of England was actually more akin to the Champagne region of eastern France, and the holy trinity of sparkling wine grapes – Pinot Noir, Pinot Meunier and Chardonnay – started to grow on suitable slopes all over Sussex. Today, there is an increasing number of impressive still wines being produced from varieties such as Bacchus, Pinot Noir and Pinot Gris. There is also an increasing number of brave growers quietly experimenting with new technology, new production techniques, grape varieties new to England and new wine styles – with exciting and promising results.

However, if you plan to grow grapes to sell to a winery, then it is important to ensure that the varieties you plant are the ones the buyer actually wants! The most popular among English winemakers are listed below; a comprehensive list can be found at **www.gov.uk/ government/collections/protected-food-name-scheme-uk-registered-products#wine** in the Protected Designation of Origin (PDO) and Protected Geographical Indication (PGI) schemes.

- **Red**: Pinot Noir, Pinot Meunier, Rondo.
- **White**: Bacchus, Madeleine x Angevine 7672, Chardonnay, Seyval Blanc, Reichensteiner, Müller-Thurgau, Ortega.

Rootstocks

There is a natural tendency when choosing rootstock and clone to hedge your bets and plant as wide a range of combinations as possible in the hope that at least one will prove the perfect match to your soil and situation. Better, perhaps, to take the time to match the soil type and climate to the best possible combination for the variety and site being planted.

The use of vines grafted onto rootstocks is now common in wine regions due to the North American Phylloxera vastatrix louse that destroyed two-thirds of European vineyards in the 1860s. Eventually it was found that American grapevines were resistant, so our own *Vitis vinifera* was grafted on to American vines. But different rootstocks have different degrees of vigour and take up nutrients at different rates, affecting grapevine growth. High vigour plants have greater yields, longer growth cycles, less sugar and higher acidity, but are more vulnerable to disease. Also, different rootstocks have different susceptibilities to nematodes, which carry plant viruses. The majority of rootstocks used today originate from crosses of three American species: *Vitis riparia*, *Vitis rupestris* and *Vitis berlandieri*. *Vitis riparia* rootstocks are low in vigour and suffer from iron deficiency (chlorosis) in chalky soils. *Vitis rupestris* rootstocks are very vigorous, with a deep rooting system, but are also very susceptible to chlorosis. *Vitis berlandieri* is very vigorous and deep rooting and has a high resistance to chlorosis. However, its cuttings have a very poor ability to root and so it is rarely used as a pure species.

The correct choice depends on many factors, including the calcium content of the soil, the vigour of the vine required, the depth of soil, water-holding capacity of the soil, soil acidity and salinity, grape variety, climate and yield and quality required. The principal rootstocks used in the UK are 5BB, SO4, 5C and 125AA. Research is underway to investigate other available ones suitable for UK climate and soils. The rootstocks included in the table are all *Vitis riparia* x *Vitis berlandieri* hybrids. Fercal is a rootstock adapted to high soil pH and is deep rooting, and has performed well on high pH soils in other wine regions. 41B rootstock is performing well in parts of East

Rootstocks used in the UK

Rootstock	Description
Gravesac	Low lime tolerance, medium vigour, good tolerance to humid (spring) soils.
101-14	Low lime tolerance, low vigour, prefers cool, deep, fertile soils and has good tolerance to humid soils, encourages early ripening.
3309C	Low lime tolerance, low vigour, suitable for cool, fertile, deep and free-draining soils, but good tolerance to humid soils, encourages early ripening. Performs well in close spacings.
SO4 (aka Binova)	Medium lime tolerance, high vigour, prefers fertile, cold soils and has a good tolerance to humid soils. Poor magnesium uptake, so will need extra Mg applications.
5BB	Medium lime tolerance, very high vigour, good tolerance to a wide range of soils, including humid, cold and fertile, may delay ripening.
125AA	Medium lime tolerance, very high vigour, suited to a wide range of soils, including humid, poorly-drained and droughty, may delay ripening.
5C	Medium lime tolerance, high vigour, adapts to a wide range of soils, but not wet or droughty soils.
161-49C	Medium lime tolerance, low vigour, prefers free-draining soils and suffers in humid soils in spring, poor uptake of magnesium.
41B	High lime tolerance, medium vigour, prefers dry, chalky soils and suffers in humid soils in spring, good for shallow soils.
Fercal	Very high lime tolerance, high vigour, prefers dry, chalky soils, high tolerance to humid soils, very poor uptake of magnesium.

Sussex because it is suited to calcareous soils with a high pH due to its lime tolerance. In calcareous soils grapevine roots cannot absorb sufficient iron to provide the vine's needs. Iron is a key component of chlorophyll and iron deficient vines have leaves that are very yellow (chlorotic). The ability to obtain adequate iron from the soil in the presence of a high concentration of calcium (limestone) is called lime tolerance.

Prices per vine decrease as the order volume increases, and with large orders of 2,000 or more, delivery is often free. Grapevines are usually imported in parcels of 25 and have plant passports attached that must be kept for one year. In the UK there is a choice of high- or low-grafted vines. High-grafted vines have a graft union at 90cm instead of 30cm and are more expensive than the low-grafted vines. However high-grafted vines reach the fruiting wire and begin to yield a year earlier and protect the vines from rabbits.

To date there is no supplier available in the UK that supplies organic grapevines grafted to organically grown rootstocks or genetically modified clones and rootstocks.

Young vines may display symptoms of 'early vine decline' but this is most often a direct result of poor site selection, poor soil preparation prior to planting the vineyard or poor weed control during the first two years after planting.

Grapevine trunk disease is caused by a complex of pathogenic fungi known as *Esca*. They include *botryosphaeria, cylindrocarpon* and *phaeoacremonium*, and are a significant problem acknowledged across the entire wine making world. Grapevine trunk disease occurs in the vineyard less as a result of diseased vines being imported from the nursery, but rather via wounds made by cutting during winter pruning over a number of years. If pruned aggressively over a period of 12–15 years, it is common to see individual vines start to die off in late summer. This is due to sap not being able to flow freely through the vine, because the vascular tissue which conducts the sap from the roots into the foliage has been (over time) compromised by wounds made at the surface of the vine which penetrate into the internal part of the vine – and the *Esca* fungi have been able to enter the vine via these pruning wounds and start to attack the inner tissue of the vine.

Case study
Site preparation — Hush Heath Vineyards, Kent
www.hushheath.com

With its half-timbered manor house dating back to 1503, its meadows, its orchards, its ancient woodland and its dreamlike setting in the heart of the Garden of England, the Hush Heath Estate near Staplehurst has a timeless beauty that isn't quite as timeless as you might think. In fact the first vines were only planted on Oast House Meadow in spring 2002, when new owner and property and hotels tycoon Richard Balfour-Lynn embarked on the estate's transformation.

The four-acre site was well protected from both the prevailing south-westerly winds and the cold north-easterly. The soil, Wealden clay over Tunbridge Wells sands, held its moisture well in dry years but badly over the winter and spring when access became difficult and the frost risk was increased.

Before planting, the rich clay was meticulously subsoiled to break up years of compaction. Old tree roots were removed and the whole site was drained with a network of underground pipes. The vines were hand-planted with the rows orientated towards the south-east and have a row width of 2.3m and 1.3m between each vine giving a vine density of 3,344 per hectare (1,354/acre). The vines were grown on a Vertical Shoot Positioned (VSP) trellis, with the fruiting wire 80cm from the ground, pruned to a two-cane horizontal Guyot system (Double Guyot) with an overall trellis height of around 2m.

The classic Champagne varieties Pinot Noir, Chardonnay and Pinot Meunier were planted using two clones of each with each clone on two different rootstocks to mitigate climatic variation and add to the complexity of the wine. The varietal mix was selected to produce top-quality rosé sparkling wine; there was therefore a slight bias towards the reds: 45 per cent Pinot Noir, 45 per cent Chardonnay and 10 per cent Pinot Meunier.

This turned out to be a fantastically successful vineyard in terms of yield and quality, so in 2007 a small plot of mainly Burgundian clones was planted in an adjoining field. These have smaller bunches and tend towards higher sugars and flavour, with correspondingly lower yields than Champagne clones. May 2008 saw yet more planting at Hush Heath, maintaining the same successful varietal mix and proportions, but with some new clone and rootstock combinations.

The gradual expansion of the vineyards was continued in 2009 when grapes were planted on 4 ha at nearby Bourne Farm in Sandhurst. There were two sites, one for Chardonnay and the other for the Pinot Noir and Pinot Meunier, both being quite steep south-facing slopes. Planting density was slightly higher than at Hush Heath, with a row width of 2.25m and 1.2m between the vines (3,703/ha). The 45/45/10 proportions of the original Hush Heath planting were again followed.

In 2011 the 2.5 ha Middle Strackney Wood, previously an orchard but fallow for two years, was planted and as with the other plantings great attention was paid to the preparation of the site. In anticipation of planting in May 2011 the site was drained and subsoiled. The row orientation was changed to north-east/south-west due to its narrow shape, giving longer rows (less turning) and to help the drainage of cold air and frost from the site. The Chardonnay, 46 per cent of the vineyard, was planted at the top of the site, which was less frost affected. Pinot Noir makes up 30 per cent of the area, including some Burgundian clones for colour and flavour. The proportion of Pinot Meunier was increased to 20 per cent, reflecting the results from the winery, which suggest that the grape is rather more interesting than was previously supposed. Out of interest, 120 of each of the old traditional Champagne varietals Petit Meslier, Arbane and Pinot Blanc were also planted (four per cent).

In charge of winemaking is Victoria Ash and Owen Elias, WineGB winemaker of the year four times with a host of international and national awards to his name, who is now consultant winemaker.

Since 2017 a major expansion progamme has been started and they now have a 200-seater tasting room, cellar door shop, commercial kitchen for weddings etc and a large roof-top terrace bar.

Clones

A clone is genetically identical to the parent, and is usually prop-agated using cuttings. Clones are selected for their performance under a number of headings including average yield, bud fertility, early or late budburst, early or late ripening, berry size, berry sugar and acidity, phenolic and aroma compounds, disease resistance, drought resistance, frost resistance, organoleptic quality and susceptibility to viruses. Clonal selection has reduced the use of other vine propaga-tion techniques such as mass selection, hybridisation and intraspecific hybrids.

The clones for UK wine production recommended by Vine-Works Ltd **www.vine-works.com** are:

- Chardonnay – **95**, **75**, **76** are high quality and low yielding, **96**, **121** are good quality with good yields. These are the most widely planted Chardonnay clones in Champagne. **809** is a Dijon/Burgundy clone and is relatively new.

- Pinot Noir – **777** has small, compact clusters, small berries and is low-yielding. **828** is a high quality and low yielding clone. **943** has the smallest berries of all the Dijon clones, low seed counts, small clusters, open bunches, low yields and higher sugar content. **GM 1-47** is a popular open cluster clone planted in Germany. **GM 20-13** clone produces smaller berries, has lower acidity grapes and is low yielding with open clusters. **GM 2-6** is a higher yielding clone that produces more open clusters. **A2107** produces open clusters and is a medium yielding clone.

- Pinot Meunier – **977**, **865**, **864** are heavy cropping clones. **We36** clone produces modest yields and **We292** is a lower yielding clone but both have open clusters.

The most common and popular Pinot Noir wine clones in Burgundy are **777** and **828**, and the reliable **115** and **667**, all of which are avail-able for still Pinot Noir wine production in the UK. There are many more clones available and the best starting point to match clone and rootstock combination is the ENTAV international catalogue – 'Cat-alogue of Selected Varieties & Certified Clones Cultivated in France'

– at **http://plantgrape.plantnet-project.org/en/clones**. There are many clones available for Pinot Noir and Chardonnay, but fewer for other grape varieties such as Bacchus, which has demonstrated hardly any differences amongst clones but is affected more by site, canopy management and crop levels. All French certified varieties and clones are listed in the ENTAV catalogue, although not all will be suitable for UK soil and climate conditions. It is extremely important to store the grapevines correctly in a cool, dark area when they arrive and before planting. Additionally they should be checked on arrival for adequate moisture and lack of mould.

Grafted grapevine suppliers

Pépinières Tourette, Les Granges 07 200 Vogüé, France
www.pepinieres-tourette.fr/en/
Stephen Skelton MW, 1B Lettice Street, London, SW6 4EH
www.englishwine.com
The Vine House, Farfield Farm, Westow, York, YO60 7LS
www.thevinehouse.co.uk
Haygrove Evolution, Redbank Farm, Little Marcle Road, Herefordshire, HR8 2JL
www.haygrove-evolution.com
Vine Works Ltd, 7 Steele Close, The Juggs, West Chiltington, West Sussex, RH20 2LL
www.vine-works.com
Vines Direct Ltd, 13 Ferneham Road, Fareham, Hants, PO15 5BT
www.vinesdirect.co.uk
Vineyard Solutions Ltd, Unit 11a, Baddow Park Estate, Great Baddow, Chelmsford, Essex, CM2 7SY
www.vineyardsolutions.co.uk

Vineyard design

After the site and grape varieties have been chosen, the vital decisions are grapevine spacing and density, and the choice of trellis/training system. These elements impact capital outlay, along with the vineyard

Case study
Site and soil preparation — Hobdens Vineyard, East Sussex
www.sussexvineyards.com/hobdens

Gerard and Jonica Fox's decision back in 2003 to found Hobdens Vineyard at Mayfield, East Sussex, as a sparkling wine producer was a forward-thinking one. The English wine industry was beginning to realise that the topography, climate and soil of much of the South-East was more akin to the Champagne region than to Germany, but few people yet understood that England could and would produce sparkling wines as good as anything the French could make.

For pioneers like the Foxes, a microscopic understanding of the terroir of their 1.5ha plot – its soil, its microclimate, its aspect, slope, elevation and drainage – was critical. It was May 2005 by the time they had completed their planning and preparation.

Having settled on the classic Champagne varieties, the Foxes needed rootstock that could cope with cool summers and clay soils, so they used SO4 (workhorse of cool climates, albeit with some issues) and 3309C (clay friendly/fruit quality enhancing) to see if they made a substantial difference in fruit quality or crop weight. They also chose mid-season ripening clones (late clones might never ripen and early clones might make harvest and winemaking logistics difficult).

They looked at various pruning styles to devise a suitable trellising plan and set their fruiting wire height quite high, to keep the fruit and young shoots safe from ground frosts. Having decided that the fruiting wire would be at 1m, it followed that the trellis height would be about 2m and that then led to relatively wide alleys at 2.3m (on later plantings this was reduced to 2.1m to increase density). Vines were planted 1.5m apart (later plantings were 1.25m) so the first field was less dense than in many other English vineyards. Plumpton College graduate Jonica was, and is, a keen advocate of yield-per-vine rather than yield-per-hectare data and saw 2.1m as the ideal width not just for density but also for mowing; and as the alley-width you start with will be with you forever, it's a decision not to be rushed into.

The first field of vines had a 7 per cent slope, faced south-south-east and was thick Wealden clay over sandstone. Clay depths varied across the vineyard from 35m+ to just 2m in one corner. Iron-rich gravels were spread in thin-layered pockets across the field at depths of 1.5m or more. Topsoils were loamy and about 15cm to 25cm deep, and with the correct pH level of 6.5. Lying on the mid-slope of a substantial hill (the vineyard was 380ft above sea level), this was quite wet land due to uphill run-off.

The site was sheltered, with light summer winds to keep the air moving, but protected from westerly gales and north-easterly winter winds. The existing hedges and individual trees within the hedgerows provided all the shelter required, although the Foxes did lift the canopy and reduce the height of five oak trees to improve light and air flow. Frost and cold air drains well, and they keep the downhill woodland clear of undergrowth so that icy air is not trapped in the field.

Soil preparation was extremely important. First they installed drainage, a herringbone pattern, 15cm diameter perforated plastic drains laid in gravel meant 25cm wide, 1.45m deep trenches, a layer of stone, the pipe, then more stone, backfilled with soil every 3m across the slope. Drainage improved immediately, but there was significant compaction after a history of use by heavy agricultural vehicles and materials that needed to be addressed, so they subsoiled the field at its driest point in August 2004, breaking up the compaction and opening up the deeper soil.

They trellised the vineyard almost immediately. Early trellising meant they had the fruiting wire in place to tie the tutor to, minimising the risk of vines blowing over or getting pulled down by rabbits. They did not expect deer, but found out the heart-breaking way that young vine shoots are gourmet food for deer. Expensive fencing went up very fast at that point!

site characteristics, so will directly affect the management of the site.

Firstly, make sure the row orientation is downhill, north–south, to allow maximum exposure to the sunlight exposure, to accelerate the cold air downflow and to prevent tractors from rolling over! Planting density (which includes row spacing and vine spacing) is a question of fine judgement: on the one hand, vines planted too far apart produce hardly any grapes or foliage. The closer they are the more vigorous they are and the higher their yields. On the other hand, you should take into account the turning circle and width of your tractor and machinery, as well as soil type, rootstock, grape variety and the type of trellis system to be installed.

There are many trellis systems available, but the Vertical Shoot Positioned (VSP) system, i.e. single and double Guyot, is common in the UK; there are other systems but they are not to be recommended as they are far too complicated and expensive to set up as well as expensive to manage. There have been a number of occasions where the Scott-Henry system has been recommended, and vineyards have been extremely badly compromised by growers trying to force this system onto vines which do not possess the required level of vigour to use this system. Scott Henry is only employed where a vineyard displays very excessive vigour, and is not therefore producing grapes, only growing foliage. Generally in England this is not the case, and most vineyards are perfectly well suited to the VSP system, albeit on varying width of alleyway. Vigorous vineyards are better off with wider alleyways, to enable humidity to dissipate and sunlight to penetrate – whilst weaker vineyards are better off on alleyways of between 2.2–2.4 meters wide. The VSP system is simple, cheap to install and easy to manage – and should be recommended in all but the most extreme cases.

The Chablis system is only used by a small number of growers in the UK. It is not widespread as it is more complicated than the Guyot system and therefore harder to train staff. Pendlebogen is a variation of the Guyot pruning system, aka Vertical Shoot Position. The difference is that instead of the fruit bearing cane being laid flat along a single horizontal wire, it is arched over one wire and down onto a lower wire positioned approx. 20 cm below. This is commonly used in the UK.

The choice of training system to be established will need to be made in conjunction with the choice of pruning style: either cane or spur pruning. Row length is also important because long rows of vines are difficult for employees to work in. It is worth developing a vineyard map with as much detail as possible regarding blocks of varieties and their location with the clones/rootstock combination before marking out and planting the vineyard.

Planting the vines

This is the big moment – but to avoid triumph turning into disaster take heed of the following dos and don'ts. Don't plant on hot, sunny, windy days when roots can be damaged during planting. Do plant the vines as soon as possible after they've been delivered, and meanwhile store them correctly. Do mark out the rows and spacing clearly beforehand, by hand and eye in a small vineyard, but using GPS and laser-guided equipment on a larger scale.

If hand planting, remember to make sure the hole is large enough to cram in the root system without damaging any part of it, and place soil around the vines, mounded, to stop any fertiliser/herbicide from damaging the young vines. If the spring is warm and dry the newly planted vines will need immediate watering to avoid water stress.

Consideration should be given to the use of grow tubes/tree guards/vine shelters that promote rapid shoot growth (but with long internodes) early in the season due to the greenhouse effect created inside the tube. It has been suggested that they encourage the vine to produce a crop in the second year, but it has also been shown to decrease overall vine growth by limiting the vine to one shoot. In many cases these tubes decrease leaf area in the first year of growth, but are useful to protect the young vines from rabbits and contact herbicide sprays. Lack of pruning or bad pruning in the first year will mean the vines will have too many buds, and allowing vines to bear grape bunches too early in their lives will affect the growth of the vascular system and roots. In some wine regions it has been established that young vine death is frequently connected with grapevines that were allowed to produce fruit in their second or third year.

Single stakes and string can be used to support the shoots in the first year, and then in the second year the cane that will become the trunk should be selected and unwanted buds removed and cordons established.

Grapevines in the UK are trained with one trunk but Rothley Wine Estate in Leicestershire was awarded the David Stanley Award from the Mercian Vineyard Association (MVA) for Innovation in 2012 for its 'Kingfisher Curtain Trellis System'. It uses a high trellis system that has two trunks, a common system in Michigan, devised by vineyard owners to counteract frost damage and graft union disease.

The trellis system must be able to hold the weight of the fully grown vine and withstand wind and machinery between the rows. It is imperative to have strong posts at the end of the rows to anchor the entire row and vines. The anchor system can be an 'H' shape or a slanted system, used in conjunction with high tensile wire which can be twisted and tied more easily than galvanized steel wire, due to its increased strength and durability. Another consideration is the type of posts to use for the trellis system, as wooden posts can be more aesthetically pleasing than steel ones but can eventually rot and need replacing sooner than steel posts. The final decision with regards to the trellis system and the materials used will be due to grape variety, canopy management, machinery usage and overall costs.

During the first two years, the vines must be trained properly, weeds must be controlled, vines must have access to adequate nutrients and diseases and insects must be treated. Once planted the vines should be sprayed with fungicides every two weeks. Additionally a suitable frost protection system should be installed to prevent damage to young vines that will make them susceptible to disease (See Chapter Three).

Vineyard equipment

Over the years capital equipment is going to be a major investment, but you don't have to buy everything you're going to need straight away. Either buy it as you need it (and secondhand equipment is often available from dealers, many of whom advertise in *Farmers Weekly* **www.fwi.co.uk** magazine or are WineGB members). There are also online retailers who hire out vineyard equipment, such as **www.vitifruitequipment.co.uk** based in Kent. If you are buying, make sure you have plenty of spare parts to hand because breakdowns always occur when you're at your busiest and can least afford any bottlenecks.

The equipment you need will depend on the size of the site and the vineyard design, but can include tractors, lawnmowers, flail-mowers, quad bikes, leaf removers and sprayers of various sizes.

The materials for planting and the trellis system can be bought from the consultants listed below. When choosing a vineyard con-sultant it is advisable to speak to other growers for recommenda-tions. Furthermore, choose a consultant who has practical vineyard management experience as well as an academic qualification in viticulture and oenology, because it is important that they fully un-derstand the effects of environmental influences as well as cultural prac-tices on the short- and long-term growth of the vine and grape berry development.

Vineyard planning and management

It has been known to take two to three years, and in some cases lon-ger, to locate a suitable site for a vineyard, but once you've found it you need to get down to some pretty serious planning. Diary planning must include financial organisation, a business plan, the gathering of local climate data, the start of viticulture education, workshops to attend, hiring a vineyard consultant and site prepa-ration before planting. It is worth bearing in mind that GIS and GPS can be used to map soils, slope, aspect and other topographic details, which can be used to plan row direction, row length, vine spacing, trellis design, soil additions, water and drainage, grape variety, clones and rootstocks. Farm insurance should be considered and, while NFU Mutual is used by many vineyards, it can pay to investigate other companies. Additional costs to include in the business plan should be health and safety compliance, staff wages and an estimate of the number of staff required. If you're not planning to build your own winery, then before planting the vines is the right time to track down a winery that will either buy your crop or make your wine for you. And start setting up vineyard records straight away detailing spray dates, to include what was sprayed, concentration and volume, vine growth information and weather data.

UK vineyard consultants

A'Court Viticulture
4 Shinners Cottages, The Level, Dittisham, Devon TQ6 0EN
www.acourtviticulture.co.uk

John Buchan Agronomy
1A Garden City, Tern Hill, Market Drayton, Shropshire TF9 3QB,
Tel: + 44(0)1630 639875, email: **john.buchan@btinternet.com**

Clemens Gmbh and Co KG
Rudolf-Diesel-Straße 854516 Wittlich, Germany
www.clemens-online.com

FAST Ltd
Crop Technology Centre, Brogdale Farm, Faversham, Kent,
ME13 8XZ
www.fastltd.co.uk

Furleigh Estate (Wine Consultants) Ltd
Salway Ash, Bridport, Dorset, DT6 5JF
www.furleighestate.co.uk

Haygrove
Redbank, Ledbury, Herefordshire, HR8 2JL
www.haygrove-evolution.com

Dr Alistair Nesbitt
www.climatewine.com

Plumpton College
Ditchling Road, nr Lewes, Plumpton, East Sussex, BN7 3AE
www.plumpton.ac.uk

Stephen Skelton MW
1B Lettice Street, London, SW6 4EH
www.englishwine.com

Dr Richard Smart
31 North Corner, Newlyn, Cornwall, TR18 5JG
www.smartvit.com.au

Three Choirs Vineyards Ltd
Newent, Gloucestershire, GL18 1LS
www.three-choirs-vineyards.co.uk

Vine Care UK
22 High Park Avenue, Hove, East Sussex, BN3 8PE
www.vinecareuk.com

Vines Direct Ltd
Blagdon, 32 Peartree Lane, Danbury, Essex, CM3 4LS
www.vines-direct-ltd.com

Vineyard Dynamics Ltd
77 Pullman Lane, Godalming, Surrey, GU7 1YB
www.vineyarddynamics.com

Vineyard Solutions Ltd
Baddow Park, West Hanningfield, Great Baddow, Chelmsford,
Essex, CM2 7SY
www.vineyardsolutions.co.uk

Vine Works Ltd
7 Steele Close, The Juggs, West Chiltington, West Sussex, RH20 2LL
www.vine-works.com

VINES DIRECT LTD

NEW VINEYARD ESTABLISHMENT

- **SITE SELECTION & SITE ASSESSMENT:** Correct choice of site is vital in the UK's northerly winegrowing climate.

- **VINEYARD DESIGN:** Design of your trellis system and density of plantation is offered as a standard part of our service.

- **PRE-PLANTATION ADVICE:** All advice and organisation of soil & site preparation works.

- **GRAPEVINE SUPPLY:** All vines sourced through one partner nursery. Proven vine establishment over many years.

- **VARIETIES, CLONES, ROOTSTOCKS:** All combinations created to suit your vineyard site and target wine styles.

- **PLANTING:** Planted by GPS guided machine, accurate to within 8mm.

- **TRELLIS MATERIALS:** We supply everything, sourced direct from the factory to ensure lowest possible prices!

YOUR VINEYARD WILL BE IN THE GROUND FOR 40 YEARS. GET IT RIGHT FIRST TIME, WITH DUNCAN MCNEILL AND VOLKER SCHEU OF VINES DIRECT LTD.

CONTACT **DUNCAN MCNEILL** ON **07972 668370** OR EMAIL **DUNCAN@MVM.UK.COM**

Let Me Tell Tell You About Whisky

By Neil Ridley & Gavin D. Smith

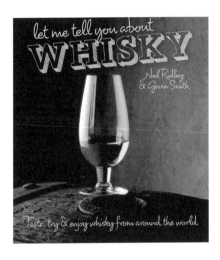

- The best whisky primer on the market
- No jargon, no snobbery and no previous knowledge assumed
- Practical details – choose, buy, serve and taste whisky with confidence
- Over 200 recommended whiskies to try from around the world with original tasting notes
- **£17.99 plus p&p**

Whisky is the world's favourite spirit and is enjoying booming sales, especially in the USA and Asia, yet too often it's shrouded in mystery, myth and complex sounding terminology. This authoritative beginner's guide cuts straight through all of this, with simple advice on how to seek out and enjoy the immense diversity of flavours and styles on offer.

The book covers not just famous Highland malts, Irish pot still whiskeys and American Bourbons, but also whiskies from South East Asia, Japan and Canada, as well as whiskies from many other producing countries, ranging from Wales through to Taiwan. There is advice on how to nose, taste and savour, how to organise a whisky tasting, which glassware to use, as well as a selection of classic whisky cocktails and advice on matching food and whisky.

This is a true beginner's guide providing a clear insight into the modern world of whisky in a way that's never been done before.

www.posthousepublishing.com

Chapter Three

The Grapes

Case Studies

T he principles of plant biology, science and chemistry help the winegrower to produce healthy grapes, quality wine and run a sustainable business. Generally UK winegrowers are very aware of their environmental responsibility, for example through the planting of native trees as a windbreak at the Rathfinny Estate, East Sussex, and biodiversity trails being designed and wild flower meadows planted around the Avonleigh Organic Vineyard, Wiltshire, as a natural method of controlling insects and pests. However, this chapter does not explain every aspect of conventional, organic or biodynamic viticulture or winemaking in the UK, but instead focuses on UK regulations, certification, European law and grape-growing methods available to UK vineyards.

The annual grapevine growth cycle

The fruitful grapevine buds burst the year after their formation after the winter dormancy period, in spring when budburst happens and shoots emerge. The energy needed for this comes from the root-stored carbohydrates from the previous year. The grapevine annual growth cycle is dependent on many cultural and environmental factors, but here is a general overview:

Seasonal vineyard activities

The correct timing and rigorous execution of seasonal vineyard activities is crucial. Issues such as staffing requirements, record keeping and equipment maintenance need to be timetabled and co-ordinated if the vineyard is to run smoothly. The vineyard's year has to be planned ahead and ought to be included in the original business plan detailing financial considerations for labour, equipment, sprays and consultancy fees.

Winter
The number of staff, costs and winter pruning technique (spur or

The annual grapevine growth cycle	
November - March	Grapevines enter into dormancy in November and begin to awaken in March when the soil (at a depth of 25cm) reaches a temperature of just over 10°C.
April - May	Sap rises and bud burst occurs followed by shoot growth and the emergence of leaves, tendrils and inflorescences. Different grape varieties and clones will start bud burst at different times. Spring frost damage can destroy the crop.
June - July	When temperatures begin to rise, flowering occurs in late May to early June (early summer). Fruitset is when the vine has flowered and fertilisation has taken place.
August - October	The grapes start to change colour - veraison (ripening) from early August. Harvest occurs in the UK in September/ October.

cane) will be determined by the vineyard size, grape variety, wine style and type of training system used.

It is important that all staff are trained in your preferred pruning requirements to leave the correct amount of buds per vine for a balanced vine that meets your optimum crop levels. The cuttings can be returned to the vineyard floor to add organic matter but might harbour diseases, or they can be burnt or pulverised (see the Environment Agency section). Pruning is done in early winter, and nearly all vineyards in the UK cane prune. Trellis maintenance is also carried out at this time.

Spring
Now's the time to tie this year's new cane or stem to the lower wire and

Hattingley Valley is a family owned winery in Hampshire producing traditional method English sparkling wines by an innovative and passionate team.

Since launching its first release in August 2013, Hattingley Valley has been recognised in competitions across the globe and developed into one of the most respected producers of English sparkling wines in the country.

Hattingley Valley offers a contract service producing award winning wines for our clients from a high quality, eco-friendly facility with full on-site laboratory services.

Over 60 gold medals and trophies awarded in major competitions (2014 - 2018)

AWARD WINNING
ENGLISH SPARKLING WINE

 01256 389188   www.hattingleyvalley.co.uk f hattingleyvalley   hattingleywines   hattingleywines

Contact: Simon Robinson, Chairman, Hattingley Valley Wines

T 01256 389188   E simon.robinson@hattingleyvalley.co.uk   www.hattingleyvalley.co.uk

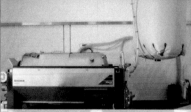

N.P. SEYMOUR

www.npseymour.co.uk
01580 712200

Leaders Drive
FENDT

Bucher Vaslin Winery Equipment

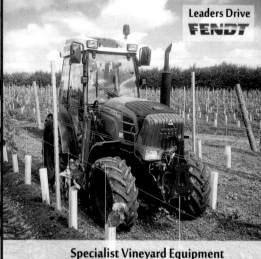

FelcoTronic Secateurs

Specialist Vineyard Equipment

Specialists in: Tractors, Machinery, Sprayers, Packing, Winery & Used Machinery
www.npseymour.co.uk   sales@npseymour.co.uk

Tank capacities 600 to 1500 litres

Vineyard Sprayers since 1895

In the years since Berthoud pioneered sprayers for French vineyards, the technology like the viticulture has moved on. With their latest Win'Air models, BERTHOUD believe that they can meet the requirements of large and small vineyards alike.

BERTHOUD®

t. 01553 774997   www.berthoud.co.uk

Forward Together

Plumpton College Wine Centre

EST. 1926

PLUMPTON
COLLEGE

The UK's centre of excellence in wine education, training and research

plumpton.ac.uk/courses/wine

University of Brighton

vigo

We're here

to help you with
your winery
equipment
requirements.

34 YEARS

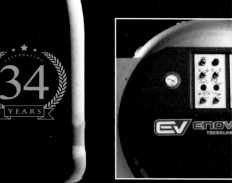

Call us on 01404 892100

Equipment • Service • Full In-house Engineering Support

It's been our privilege to serve wine producers like you over the last 34 years. We're proud of how
far we've come and what we have achieved. We carefully choose the manufacturers we work with.
Our standards may be known to be high, but our values mean everything to us and we won't
support equipment that we don't rate highly ourselves. If you need to upgrade your equipment, or
you are planning your winery set-up, please give us a call to see how we can help you.

www.vigoltd.com sales@vigoltd.com @VigoLtd 🐦

to rub off any buds growing on the trunk to inhibit the growth of water shoots and suckers. Pruning should be complete by the end of March when fertiliser and manure are spread and any other soil nutrients are applied. Clods must be broken up by hoeing, and new vines are planted and sprayed to protect against insects and fungal disease. As spring merges into summer and the days lengthen and warm up, budburst signals the start of the new growing season!

Summer

In early summer the grapevine flowers emerge. After fruitset, canopy management (including leaf removal, whether mechanically or by hand) allows airflow, spray and sunlight access to the fruiting zone to achieve optimum ripening. Shoot tipping/topping and tucking in of shoots maintain the canopy at the correct height; at the same time all unwanted lateral growth around the fruiting zone is removed.

Depending on the weight of the crop, some vineyard practice 'green harvesting' while the fruit is changing colour ('veraison'), nipping out the slower clusters so that the rest ripen evenly. (Don't waste the green bunches, though: they can be pressed to make 'verjus', a fresher alternative to vinegar.) Further spraying is carried out until the four weeks leading up to harvest. This is also the time for vintage preparation: cleaning the winery equipment, servicing all the various bits of machinery, buying laboratory analysis equipment and supplies, and finding a good crew of pickers.

Autumn

In September, as the countdown to harvesting ticks away, the grapes are sampled regularly to monitor phenols, sugar and acidity. When they have reached the levels required for the wine style, they can be picked, and after that the winemaking begins.

Organic grape growing

The fashion for organic production has long passed its peak but is still preferred by many growers. The founders of the organic movement were chiefly concerned with maintaining the health and fertility of the soil itself and modern organic farming methods, according to the EU, "combine best environmental practices, a high level of biodiversity, the preservation of natural resources and a production method in line with the preference of certain consumers for products produced using natural substances and processes."

A research-based understanding of soil science, crop growing and ecology has developed out of early organic farming methods, say its proponents, and it's far more today than simply avoiding chemical sprays. An organic vineyard owner needs to understand the causes of disease infections as well as the type, timing and concentration of treatments. In the UK the best-known organic certifying body is the Soil Association, but there are others including Organic Farmers & Growers and the Biodynamic Association. Each body has different criteria (and fees), and indeed a different understanding of wine production. However they all set the standards that vineyards must abide by to gain accreditation, as well as advice and guidance.

The Soil Association is registered with Defra and has certified farms, foods and other products and processing as organic since 1973 under the terms of EU Regulation 834/2007. Certification starts at £708 plus VAT. This includes the application fee, first inspection and full range of services for a year. There is an additional licence fee for on-site processors such as wineries that is based on your total organic sales for the year. The full Soil Association organic standards for farming and growing were revised in January 2012 and can be found online at **www.soilassociation.org/what-we-do/organic-standards/**. Additionally, the association produces details of its fee structure in its information packs, and can be contacted by telephone (Tel +44 (0)117 9142406) or via their website **www.soilassociation.org**.

Organic Farmers & Growers Ltd (OF&G) is another certification body accredited by Defra, and is approved to inspect organic production and processing in the UK. In addition, OF&G works with the Association for Organic Recycling (AfOR) and Renewable Energy Assurance Ltd (REAL) on the inspection and certification of compost and biofertiliser (from anaerobic digestion) respectively. The

OF&G *Organic Standards and Certification Manual* is available online at **http://ofgorganic.org/certification-statement/** (Tel +44 (0)1939 291800).

New EU regulations respecting organic wines have applied since the 2012 harvest. These require bottle labels to carry the EU organic logo and the code number of their certifying body in addition to national labelling requirements. The new regulations also govern production methods and what supplementary ingredients are allowed: for instance, producers using the EU organic seal cannot use ascorbic acid but can use sulfur dioxide (SO^2) for preservation but in lesser amounts than in conventionally made wine. (It is possible that the EU will ban the use of SO^2 as a biocide in the future, and research into alternative biocide products is under way.) Full details of the regulations can be found on **https://ec.europa.eu/agriculture/organic/eu-policy/eu-rules-on-production/wine_en**.

The key differences between organic and non-organic vineyard management can broadly be divided into three areas, each equally vital to success:

1. Weeds need to be controlled in the vineyard, especially if the vines are young. While the rows can be mowed, the area under the vines needs a more labour-intensive solution. There are many options for dealing with this task, including compost or fabric mulches, strimmers, tractor-mounted cultivating machines or flame weeders. Each option has its good and bad points but none provides the perfect answer. Apart from fabric mulches, all of the options mean more man-hours in the vineyard over the summer, and in fact this is one of the main extra costs in an organic vineyard. Do not expect perfectly clean, weed-free strips if you are growing organically!

2. The use of agrochemicals in organic vineyards is limited to sulfur and copper. There are other permitted inputs, such as biodynamic preparations, potassium bicarbonate and plant extracts, but the spray programme for an organic vineyard will be much simpler (and cheaper) than for a non-organic vineyard. It is also less effective at controlling mildew, though, so it is important

to practise good canopy management and regularly check the vines. Unlike some fungicides, sulfur and copper are not systemic. It is absolutely essential therefore to maintain a good spray programme and not extend the interval between sprays or miss one when you go on holiday. Any disease outbreak is very hard to control and usually means removing infected material from the site. Organic disease control relies on prevention rather than cure, and also on keeping the vines healthy by maintaining good soil. Air movement around the vines can reduce humidity and disease, so consider this when deciding vine spacing and the positioning of windbreaks, and avoid areas where the vines may be too sheltered.

3.   The absolute key to successful organic farming is the soil itself. Healthy soil will grow healthy plants. The focus is on soil biology as well as soil chemistry. Modern chemical fertilisers are designed to dissolve rapidly in the soil so that they can be readily taken up by the plant roots. The application of these chemicals leads to sudden changes in soil pH, which can reduce the populations of soil microorganisms. This is made worse still by the use of herbicides. All life in the soil (including plant roots) is interdependent, so a depletion of bacteria will cause changes higher up the food web. In an organic vineyard, soil fertility is maintained by addition of composts and manures that take longer to incorporate into the soil, feeding the soil bacteria rather than directly feeding the vines. A healthy living soil will break down dead plant material and make nutrients available to the vines. Because additions of compost and manure are relatively slow acting, the soil fertility inputs need to be considered some time in advance. Any additions will have an effect over three years, so regular inputs should be added rather than waiting until there is a nutrient deficiency. Green manures are often used to perform a variety of soil improvements. Some are deep rooting, while some fix nitrogen, attract insects or suppress weeds.

Choice of grape varieties is important and while ultimately the choice will depend on the quality and style of wine you want to make, some claim to have better disease resistance than others. Don't select a variety just for its disease resistance, though – it has to make good wine as well!

All plots or parcels to be designated organic will have to be registered and inspected by an organic certifier for three years before the grapes can be marketed as such. During this period the grapes or wine can be sold as 'in conversion.' A newly planted vineyard will crop in the third or fourth year, by which time it will have completed conversion.

Yields may be slightly lower than in non-organic vineyards. This reduction can be minimised by good disease control and regular maintenance of soil fertility. However, in practice there will often need to be some removal of grapes where mildew gets a foothold and, as maintaining soil fertility is less precise, consistently getting good yields is more difficult.

There are obvious savings in aspects of organic wine production, the main one being the increasing costs of pesticides and fertilisers. However, this is offset by the additional labour required for weed control and canopy management. Overall the cost of organic grape growing is likely to be slightly more than non-organic growing.

In the winery, organic production differs from non-organic winemaking in only a few aspects, mainly the lower limits for sulphites and the avoidance of certain fining agents. In 2012, EU organic winemaking regulations were introduced, setting out minimum EU-wide standards for wineries for the first time. One advantage of these rules was that growers are allowed to use the term 'organic wine' on labels as long as the winery is certified organic (as well as the vineyard), and also carry a new organic symbol. Ultimately, site, soil type and grape variety will determine the quality of the fruit. These basics have to be right. Choosing to go organic adds another layer to the complex mixture of factors to consider.

Case study
Organic pioneer — Sedlescombe Vineyard, East Sussex
www.englishorganicwine.co.uk

Sedlescombe Vineyard started life in 1978 as a single vine planted in a greenhouse on the 10 acres near Robertsbridge, East Sussex, that a young and idealistic Roy Cook had inherited four years earlier. Roy was living in a caravan on the site that he hoped, having watched *The Good Life* on TV, would be big enough to make him a self-sufficient organic market gardener. Like Tom and Barbara Good, Roy made his own country wines, and when he heard that a neighbouring vineyard was selling a very well-received English wine to a local restaurant, he thought he'd look seriously into the question of becoming England's first organic commercial vineyard.

The first thing he discovered was that about 1.5 acres of his market garden would make an ideal vineyard: gently sloping, south facing, sheltered from cold northerlies and well drained. That winter, after the neighbouring vineyard's harvest, Roy volunteered to work on the pruning – provided he could keep the prunings. His haul turned out to include 2,000 viable cuttings, which he promptly planted, and of which 1,000 are bearing to this day. They're Reichensteiners, a popular variety in the early days of English viticulture when growers thought that as our climate was similar to the Rhine's, perhaps German vines would suit it best.

With his German vines safely planted, Roy headed off to get some experience in German vineyards alongside his German wife Irma, returning with a secondhand German basket press. His next major planting was four acres of another popular German-derived variety, Müller-Thurgau, along with others tried and trusted in English vineyards such as Ortega and Seyval Blanc.

A big replanting programme in 2001–2003 came just too early for the English industry's switch from the German-style old favourites to the classic Champagne trinity of Chardonnay, Pinot Noir and Pinot Meunier. Roy and Irma had already been making sparkling wine since the 1980s –

another area in which Sedlescombe was a pioneer – but using the Seyval Blanc so keenly advocated by English wine guru Stephen Skelton. "Seyval Blanc can produce some very thin, uninteresting wines," says Roy, "but provided it isn't allowed to overcrop, it's a very good variety."

During their big replanting they focused on disease-resistant varieties and, to this day, have only four rows of Pinot Noir in the vineyard at nearby Bodiam, which they've been renting since 1994. Sedlescombe does make Champagne-style sparkling wine, but they buy in the grapes from other growers. Where they are, once again, blazing a trail is in the planting of red varieties such as Regent, Rondo and Dornfelder. So does Roy believe that red table wines – currently accounting for a mere 10 per cent of English output – are going to be the next big thing? Will climate change enable English growers to succeed with Mediterranean varieties such as Syrah, Grenache Noir, Cinsault, Mourvedre and Nebbiolo?

"Maybe not just yet," says Roy, "but we've had one or two exceptional years just recently, especially 2011 when we had a dry beginning and end to the season and a very hot October, which gave us not much quantity but exceptional quality. My Regent went to 12 per cent natural sugar. So maybe red isn't a big thing yet, but there are some very nice ones around. In 2016 we had 14 per cent natural alcohol on our Solaris variety and made something few growers in England have managed to do - a dessert wine! In all, almost 2,000 half bottles were produced."

In April 2018 Roy and Irma sold the vineyard to Sophie and Kieran Balmer who are local to the area; having lived in Eastbourne since 2008. Being a pair of food fans, it was only a matter of time before they became interested in wine – visiting wine areas from Provence to Stellenbosch to the Salinas Valley has allowed them to start learning about the science and art involved in winemaking. The opportunity arose to make an exciting life change that allowed them to invest in an established, independent local business, and which they simply couldn't resist!

Biodynamic grape growing

Biodynamic grape growing and winemaking adheres to the teachings of Rudolf Steiner in the 1920s, and combines planetary, homeopathic and astrological techniques. Vineyards wishing to grow grapes using biodynamic methods can contact the Biodynamic Association (BDA), which also operates an organic certification scheme: **www.biodynamic.org.uk.**

The BDA was founded in 1929 to promote biodynamic farming and gardening. It administers the Demeter symbol and gives support through a network of advisers, a journal called *Star & Furrow*, a newssheet, conferences, seminars and workshops. The Association's main objectives are to foster and promote Steiner's farming method and to help and support growers wishing to put them into practice. Further details about Demeter can be found on **www.demeter.net**.

Sustainable grape growing

Some UK vineyards are members of the environment and wildlife organisation LEAF (Linking the Environment and Farming – **www.leafuk.org**). LEAF is a practical organisation that helps with farm audits to identify ways to enhance biodiversity while still farming efficiently, such as leaving grass strips (beetle banks) around the edge of the vineyard. The Waste & Resources Action Programme also works with vineyards and wineries to reduce production waste, improve the collection of recycling materials and advise on recycling organic waste and recovering energy **www.wrap.org.uk**. Further advice and help can be sought from Sustain **www.sustainweb.org** which is an alliance for better food and farming. Sustain represents about 100 national public interest organisations working at international, national, regional and local level. It formed when the National Food Alliance and the Sustainable Agriculture Food and Environment (SAFE) Alliance merged. Occasionally there are grants for UK farming and forestry for sustainability, processing and manufacturing efficiency from the Rural Development Programme for England, Defra. More information can be found at **www.defra.gov.uk** and **www.innovateuk.org**.

The Environment Agency

The main aims of the Environment Agency are to protect and improve the environment, and promote sustainable development. It has the central role in delivering the environmental priorities and policies of central government and the Welsh Government. UK grape growers must adhere to certain environmental regulations, including the burning of vine pruning cuttings. Although some vineyards simply leave pruning cuttings in the vineyard, this practice allows for the transmission and overwintering of some pests and diseases. All UK vineyard-owners burning pruning cuttings must have registered an exemption with the Environment Agency. Vineyards that registered before 6 April 2010 will have registered a Paragraph 30 exemption. The exemption system changed in April 2010 so anybody registering an exemption after that needs to register a D7, which is a 'Burning waste in the open' exemption. The details for this can be found at **www.gov.uk/guidance/waste-exemption-d7-burning-waste-in-the-open**.

For those pulverising pruning cuttings in the vineyard, a T6 exemption is required. If vineyards spread green compost (to PAS 100 standards) under vines, the person who actually does the spreading needs to register an Agricultural Waste Exemption. The T23 exemption covers the composting of plant matter, but spreading should be carried out under either a U10 exemption or a standard rules permit, unless the compost has reached end of waste status. Any animal manure that has a natural plant-based bedding material in it (straw, hemp or sawdust) is not waste when spread on land as a fertiliser, even if it has been imported onto the farm. Further guidance for these waste management practices can be sought from the Environment Agency at **www.gov.uk/government/organisations/environment-agency** or through the WineGB website.

Basic Payment Scheme

In 2015 the Basic Payment Scheme replaced the Single Payment Scheme and UK vineyards can apply for this. Full details as to how to apply can be found at **www.gov.uk/claim-rural-payments**. In 2018 this stands at £210 per Ha but with Brexit now coming into force, this scheme will be phased out and UK vineyards will not be able to take advantage of it any longer.

Environmental Stewardship Scheme (ES)

If a UK vineyard is registered on the Rural Land Register (RLR), then it may be eligible for the Environmental Stewardship Schemes managed by Natural England on behalf of Defra. It is available to farmers and land managers in England. Full details can be found at **www.gov.uk/government/collections/environmental-stewardship-guidance-and-forms-for-existing-agreement-holders**.

Glasshouses and polytunnels

Grapevines, just like any other fruits, can be grown perfectly well in glasshouses or greenhouses with proper irrigation and air circulation. But somehow it seems like cheating, and of all 500-odd English vineyards only Strawberry Hill in Gloucestershire has really taken advantage, growing Merlot, Pinot Noir, Chardonnay and Cabernet Sauvignon under glass and even producing port-style fortified wine. Further advice and vines for growing in glasshouses can be sought from local nurseries including Grove Nurseries **www.grovesnurseries.co.uk** and Sunnybank Vine Nursery **www.sunnybankvines.co.uk**. Vines will also thrive in polytunnels, which you can buy online from a number of suppliers including **www.polytunnels.co.uk**, **www.premierpolytunnels. co.uk** and **www.firsttunnels.co.uk**.

You don't usually need planning permission for greenhouses or polytunnels, but there are exceptions that need checking with the local authority. If there is less than 20m between the polytunnels and the road, if the structure is over 3m high (or more than 4m if it has a pitched roof), if your site has a listed building or is in a conservation area, national park or area of outstanding natural beauty, then you will need to seek guidance from the local council authority and may require planning permission.

Artificial climate control means you can grow either wine or table grapes from much hotter regions with every chance of success;

Chatsworth Estate in Derbyshire produces its own glasshouse-grown grapes. These are the Muscat of Alexandria variety, grown in Spain, France, Chile and South Africa. The greenhouse at Hampton Court Palace has the biggest grapevine in the world – a Black Hamburg.

Vineyard record keeping

It is crucial to keep records of all vineyard work carried out. All events including budburst, flowering, fruitset, weather and frost occurrences should be documented for future years. Exact details of spraying must be recorded, with dates, amount and method of application, calibration details, volume used and number of applications. Details of any assessment of bud fruitfulness, pruning weights, disease symptoms, disease cycles, vine nutrition, crop assessment, canopy management methods/timing, bird protection, berry/cluster ripening datum and harvest weights and ripeness datum must be recorded. There is software available for vineyard record keeping and management from overseas companies such as CropTrak, eSKYE Sureharvest and Vingro (Vinsight Software), but to reduce costs vineyards can easily set up their own record-keeping system using Excel spreadsheets. Other UK based systems include Gatekeeper and Muddy Boots. Home made Excel spreadsheets are just as effective for most growers.

Vineyard weed control

As with many vineyard practices, your weed control method will depend on costs, labour, equipment and the size of the vineyard. Young vines are sensitive to weed and cover crop competition, but cultivation is the preferred way of suppressing weeds as it is important not to damage vine roots or trunks with equipment or chemicals. Hoeing or using rotary tillers (on loose soil) or cultivators around the vines and between the rows are the best option and should be performed when the weeds are small. Flails can damage vine trunks and increase the risk of disease, but disks and mowers can be used between rows. Suppliers of this equipment include Richard Burton Specialised Machinery **www.rbsm.me.uk** and Vitifruit Equipment

www.vitifruitequipment.co.uk. New and used equipment can be found advertised in trade magazines such as *Farmers Weekly* **www.fwi. co.uk**.

Forget any woven fabrics or reflective products or synthetic mulches as these do not work. Weeds in the alleyway can be suppressed by tractor mounted cultivators in the first year or two years. At the end of year one or year two simply sew a green cover in the alleyways (grass or a cover crop) and then mow this the following season. Under the vines, weeds are controlled either by herbicides, but increasingly by tractor mounted 'undervine cultivators'. These avoid the use of herbicide and mean that weed control can be done in windy weather – whereas spraying herbicides can only be done in calm weather to avoid spray drift on to the vines. Also, consumers are increasingly demanding that wine be made from grapes grown in more environmentally sustainable ways – thus herbicide free weed control is becoming far more popular. There has been huge progress made in the development of these tools in the last ten years and this is increasingly seen as the future of weed control.

Further legislation and guidance for all herbicide use can be found in the code of practice for all professional users of plant protection products in England and Wales in respect of Part III of the Food and Environment Protection Act 1985 (FEPA), and the regulations controlling pesticides, particularly plant protection products, under that part of the Act. The Health & Safety Executive website has advice, guidance, regulations and the full code of practice at **www. hse.gov.uk/pesticides/**. The non-selective herbicide glyphosate can control broadleaf weeds when they appear, but should not be used near young vines, and care should be taken not to damage the leaves or shoots of vines with spray drift. The UK has a limited range of contact and residual herbicides available for use on grapevines, even though some herbicides have been approved for other crops.

Frost protection
Good site selection is the most effective way of preventing spring frost damage, but thick hedges or solid fences as windbreaks won't pro-

tect the vines from frost. Late spur pruning can delay budburst, and leaving extra canes on the vine at pruning means they can be used if frost damage occurs on other canes. Training the vines high can lift the buds out of the risk of ground frost; scraping mulch away to leave bare soil under the vines allows geothermal heat to rise through the canopy.

The best way to avoid frst damage is to avoid planting in a frost prone site. If the site is frost prone the vineyard will be cold, and will not produce economically viable crops of grapes.

An overhead water-sprinkling system can be installed that freezes the young shoots, ensuring they do not fall below 0°C. Waste water from the winery could be recycled for an overhead frost-protection system. Grapevines can also be sprayed with a polymer coating containing chitosan and chitin, a natural alternative that triggers the defensive mechanisms in plants and is sold in some nurseries and garden centres as well as online at **www.travena.co.uk/softguard-plant-health-care**. Permanent fans can be installed in the vineyard, but these can be noisy for your neighbours if they are close by. Alternatively fans can be tractor-mounted, but this requires a qualified tractor driver available during the night and early morning and, again, the noise at night can cause issues with neighbours.

Oil heaters, agricultural burners, stopgel candles, bougies, smudge pots or braziers are also popular for frost protection, but some of these produce smoke that can cause problems for nearby properties. Stopgel candles require staff to be available at unsociable hours to ignite and extinguish them, which can be worthwhile if it prevents crop damage and loss. It is far better to have many smaller heaters in the vineyard than a couple of large ones, in order to heat the vineyard evenly. Albury Organic Vineyard in Surrey has converted an old corn-drying machine to continually suck in cold air at ground level and send it skywards. This should create enough air movement in the lowest part of the vineyard to fight off the worst frosts. It is used in tandem with other frost-prevention equipment that includes a Frost-Guard machine **www.agrofrost.eu/**, which blasts warm air around the vineyard, and hundreds of bougies (paraffin heaters) that they put in rows near to the vines. Vitifruit Equipment also supplies an electric cable anti-frost system (basically central heating for vines), which is expensive to install but worth considering for a large commercial vineyard as it is automatic and cheap to run **www.vitifruitequipment.co.uk**.

Weather monitoring

A vineyard's specific microclimate will count hugely towards its triumph or its failure. Closely monitoring the weather in the vineyard itself will enable the manager to make evidence-based decisions regarding spray timing and frost protection, save time and money, enhance grape quality and boost the final yield. A large vineyard will want its own weather stations to monitor air temperature, relative humidity, wind and rainfall. Hush Heath Vineyards in Kent have weather stations installed that send SMS alerts to mobile phones that can even warn of disease incidence such as powdery mildew and downy mildew. This means the vineyard can fight specific diseases with targeted sprays, resulting in less spraying. Suppliers of weather stations include **www.weathershop. co.uk** and **www.weatherstations.co.uk**, and **www.weatherquest.co.uk** offers web-based weather forecasts for farms. Historical vineyard weather records, especially at key points in the growing season such as budburst and flowering, should be included in the vineyard records.

Common vineyard diseases

There are many vineyard diseases, but the main ones are powdery mildew, downy mildew and *Botrytis cinerea*. As with every wine region in the world, grapevine trunk disease has become more recognisable and widespread. Most vineyards use a preventative-spraying programme, including organic growers who use a permitted sulfur and copper spray. Noble rot produces dessert wines, but grey rot causes rotten fruit that decreases the final wine quality. *Botrytis cinerea* fungal disease attacks all parts of the vine all year round but is more predominant if it rains near to harvest and at >90 per cent humidity. It attacks flowers during pollination and is especially problematic when grapes are ripening, so fungicides are sprayed. Canopy management is especially important to let the air flow into the fruit zone, and choosing clones with looser bunches is recommended. Powdery mildew is a fungal disease that likes warm, shady, dry conditions and affects fruit set and yield, reduces berry size and colour and produces a mildew flavour. Downy mildew is a fungal disease that likes warm humid summers. Growers can consult the approved list of pesticides and their permitted uses at **www.hse.gov.uk/biocides/copr/**.

Spraying regulations and qualifications

Most UK commercial vineyards use air-assisted broadcast sprayers to apply fungicides and herbicides, although tunnel sprayers are used by a couple of the larger vineyards. The smaller vineyards use hydraulic sprayers and smaller, cheaper backpack sprayers. The label recommendations on the sprays must allow for all these methods, and it is extremely important to follow all the manufacturer's instructions with regards to dosage and timing of application.

It is a legal requirement for anyone spraying fungicides or pesticides to hold a City & Guilds Land certificate of competence (a spraying certificate or a pesticide licence). Tractor-driving courses are available at relevant colleges and the NPTC website **www.nptc. org.uk** has a list of centres across the country where the PA1, PA3 and PA6 (the main ones needed for UK vineyards) can be taken. PA1 is the first introductory course to spraying covering calibration, equipment, safe storage, waste disposal and health and safety. No further pesticide application (PA) qualifications can be taken until it has been passed and no spray qualifications from any other country are accepted in the UK.

If using pesticides in a vineyard it is important to remember that some plant-protection products have an aquatic buffer zone requirement when applied by horizontal boom or broadcast air-assisted sprayers. If the aquatic buffer zone is to be reduced then it is your legal obligation to carry out and record a Local Environment Risk Assessment for Pesticides (LERAP). For horizontal boom sprayers it is only possible to reduce buffer zones of five metres; buffer zones greater than this cannot be reduced. If you just want to apply the buffer zone specified on the label you do not have to carry out a LERAP. However, you are legally obliged to record this decision as is normal in your spray records, as advised in section 6 of the updated Code of Practice for Using Plant Protection Products. It is a statutory code of practice, which means that it can be given in evidence if you are prosecuted for a breach of pesticide laws.

The code gives practical advice on how to use pesticides lawfully. You can also become a member of a professional body, the National Register of Sprayer Operators, run by BASIS, and gain certificates in competence of storage and sale. BASIS is an independent organisation set up at the suggestion of the UK government in 1978 to establish and assess standards in the pesticide industry relating to storage, transport and competence of staff. The Crop Protection Association (CPA) **www.cropprotection.org.uk** produces a series of guidance leaflets on best practice for pesticide use through the Voluntary Initiative **www.voluntaryinitiative.org.uk**, covering issues such as avoiding drift, emergency procedures and nozzle selection. Other CPA publications include *Keeping residues well within the limits*; *Working within the pesticide residue limit*; *Every drop counts – keeping water clean*; *For the benefit of biodiversity*; and *Integrated crop management*.

It is a legal requirement to keep detailed spray records with dates, amounts, concentration and method of application, and the format of all records should be in place before starting. Further details about record keeping and Control of Substances Hazardous to Health (COSHH) are found on the health and safety executive website **www.hse.gov.uk/coshh**. UK agronomists that can help include Agrii **www.agrii.co.uk** and Hutchinsons **www.hutchinsons-online.co.uk**. Specialist spray equipment can be bought from Micron sprayers **www.micron.co.uk**, Vitifruit Equipment: **www.vitifruitequipment. co.uk** and from new and used suppliers advertising in *Farmers Weekly* **www.fwi.co.uk**. Only buy pesticides, fungicides and insecticides that have been approved for storage and use on grapevines in the UK. Look for the Defra, MAPP or HSE approval number on the label on the container. Beware of offers of cheap pesticides as these may be illegal unapproved products.

Some organic sprays containing seaweed for plant health have been approved by the organic certification bodies for use on organic crops but you still need to check whether that includes UK grapes destined for wine production. WineGB members are regularly notified of Specific Off-label Approvals for specific pests or disease such as 'Justice' for powdery mildew and 'Option' for downey mildew. ADAS is an independent, science-based environmental and rural consultancy and contracting services to agriculture and the food and drinks industry throughout the UK and internationally **www.adas. co.uk** and can help UK vineyards. It is also worth checking the Food and Environment Research Agency website **www.fera.defra.gov. uk**, particularly with regards to food, drink, plant and environment research in the UK.

Common pests in the UK

Red spiders are distressingly common in glasshouses and polytunnels, but Erineum mites are often visible as blisters on leaves on outdoor grapevines. Wasps are a major problem on thin-skinned and early ripening varieties, and can cause more than mere annoyance for pickers as well. Birds are a problem as harvest approaches and there are various ways to deter them. Bird netting is available from **www.birdgard. co.uk** and **www.birdcontrol.co.uk** and can be placed across whole rows, whole blocks or just down the sides of the rows over the fruiting zone. Bird netting is made from UV-resistant polypropylene and lasts up to 10 years, and it is important to get the finest mesh to stop smaller birds from getting in. It can be expensive, due to the added cost of putting on and taking off and the equipment needed, i.e. tractor and winder, plus the labour required. However, in the long run it can prevent considerable crop loss!

Some countries have started using birds of prey to scare birds, but if by some chance you aren't a qualified falconer then another option is to use Helikites or helium balloons that mimic raptors. See **www. allsopphelikites.com**. Other bird-scaring methods include scarecrows, reflective tapes and old compact discs, electronic bird scarers and scare guns. The noise the last two make will probably be unpopular with close neighbours! All bird-scaring methods must obey UK regulations for wildlife control management and control of birds, which can be found on the Natural England website: **www.naturalengland.org.uk/ourwork/regulation/wildlife**.

Rabbits can destroy a vineyard with amazing speed, so tree guards can be used to protect young shoots: different colours can have different effects but it is best to use ones with ventilation holes. Organic methods include a natural repellent containing garlic, which wild rabbits dislike. They are also not keen on lavender, which could be planted in the vineyard as a deterrent.

The best way to keep deer out is by fencing, but it is expensive to install both in materials and labour. Electric fences are cheaper and easier to install, and can be powered by solar energy if the vineyard is far from a power source. The shock is not lethal to deer but it will surprise them! Pheasants can be a problem in newly planted vineyards and those with low bearing fruit, but good deer fencing usually keeps them out too. If the vineyard owner has a shooting licence this is an option during the pheasant-shooting season!

WineSkills offers master classes on pest and disease management, but it is also advisable to set up an Integrated Pest Management (IPM) system even before planting your vineyard. IPM is used to prevent disease and pest infestation, to monitor infestation and to intercede when necessary with as few chemicals as possible (and no poisons). Vineyard consultants and agronomists such as Agrii (**www. agrii.co.uk**) can help with the planning and implementation of an IPM programme.

Maximising yields

Achieving consistently good yields is a major challenge for UK vineyards, but we are lucky to be able to learn from other wine regions of a similarly cool climate. The UK has lower yields than other regions, but we are slowly improving. The most important thing is to get the basics right from the very beginning, including site selection, soil and vine nutrition and management, soil structure, drainage, pruning and canopy management. But there's no getting round the fact that the single most important limiting factor is weather at flowering.

The northerly latitude creates growing conditions in which less heat is accumulated during the growing season, which results in fruit buds containing on average fewer bunches, and the bunches are a smaller size. The south coast of England is at 51° north, while the most southerly wine growing regions in the world lie at around 45° south. In addition to this, poor management of soil nutrition levels (especially potash) and excessive soil compaction are also blamed for English vineyards failing to come up to their potential. And it is important to remember that soil nutrient levels on their own do not indicate the availability of nutrients for uptake by the vine. This is because nutrient availability is affected by both acidity and rootstock choice; so soil analysis must be carried out in conjunction with leaf or petiole analysis.

High sunlight in the canopy will affect plant growth regulators by increasing cytokinin levels but decreasing gibberellin, which improves grape quality from the reduced growth of the vegetative parts of the vine. The timing and assiduity of vineyard practices is important as well as attention to pest and disease control. According to Chris Foss of Plumpton College, the most common reason for yield fluctuation is cool weather in June when the vines are flowering. This causes a drop in the sugars produced by photosynthesis just when the vine is steadily growing. The resulting shortfall in carbohydrates will affect the fertilisation of flowers and the setting of fruit, thus reducing the yield for the coming vintage. However, it will also affect the initiation of flowers in the buds that will open the following year, which reduces the number of bunches each shoot will carry in the subsequent spring, so both the next harvest and the following one are affected.

We cannot control our weather, but we can help to minimise the impact of wind and frost. Yield prediction techniques prior to harvest are important for winery planning, record keeping and harvest organisation. The yield prediction will depend upon several factors shown in the diagram on page 71.

Precision viticulture

Precision Viticulture (PV) has had a faltering start in the UK. The idea is very interesting but the industry is not yet of a size where it can be practically applied. Where PV is used overseas, machine harvesters record yield in real time, and use the data to create yield maps of the vineyard. These yield maps are then used to home in and focus on improving less productive areas. Until we start using mechanical harvesters then PV will be restricted to soil nutrient mapping using GPS. It is far more important to get the basics of vineyard management correct before moving onto the next level of PV. This is a real problem in English viticulture – the basic foundation knowledge is often not being taught or communicated – growers do not have a sound grasp of basic grapevine physiology but wish to focus on PV and disease forecasting models. Until we have a better foundation knowledge of viticulture in the English wine industry, such topics as precision viticulture should be left alone. Do not run before you can walk.

Harvest organisation

Good, clear communication between the winery and the vineyard, whether you have your own winery on site or you're sending the grapes away to be vinified, make for a smooth, efficient and stress-free operation, especially in the lead-up to harvest.

While the winery staff are servicing and cleaning the press, the pumps and all the other equipment and ensuring that they have all the process aids, chemicals and laboratory equipment they're going to need in stock, the vineyard staff will be monitoring the ripeness of the grapes. Ideally, the same person should sample the grapes at the same time of day at least once a week and test for pH, sugar (remembering any necessary temperature adjustment), titratable acidity (TA g/l) and bunch/cluster weights.

On a commercial scale, sampling whole clusters is more representative than taking 100 individual berries from across each block. Sample the top and bottom of a slope separately. You will need a

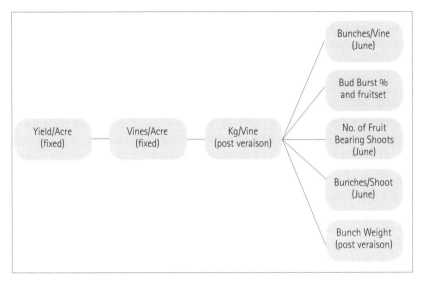

Factors that affect final yield at harvest.

pH meter, a thermometer, a hydrometer and refractometer, as well as a set of scales. The actual organisation of the grape harvest from buying enough picking bins and secateurs, hiring and organising grape pickers, training and equipping enough first-aiders, deciding which varieties to pick first and, crucially, arranging transport for the grapes from the vineyard to winery are all decisions that need to be made in advance.

The manager should make a habit of walking the vineyard blocks tasting the grapes and checking for disease as often as possible. Late season disease will affect juice and wine quality, and discarding all the affected bunches can be done either by the pickers in the vineyard or on arrival at the winery – although a contract winemaker won't thank you for sending diseased bunches, so if you're selling grapes or sending them to be vinified they should be sorted before they leave the vineyard.

Weather monitoring is of utmost importance at this time as heavy rain will dilute the berries and can cause splitting, as well as turning the vineyard into a mudbath where trucks, cars and trailers can get stuck.

Keep records of the yield and picking date per block, of each variety per acre/hectare as well as harvest ripeness indicators including acidity, sugar and pH. These can be useful in future years to estimate harvest dates. Other information you should collect includes average cluster weight and total yield per variety and per block, which can be done either in the vineyard or the fruit can be weighed upon arrival at the winery. Harvest record keeping is a legal requirement and is essential for the Wines Standards branch of the Food Standards Agency; forms are available from its website, **www.food. gov.uk/business-industry/winestandards/winestandardsresources**, and on the members section of the WineGB website.

Regional Wine Standards Board representatives can also supply hard copies of the forms. Vineyards that don't make wine need to complete a WSB 12 Harvest Declaration, including the continuation sheet WSB 15 Commercial Accompanying Document. Wine producers may also need WSB 10 Notification of Enrichment, WSB 14 De-acidification of Wine and WSB 15 Commercial Accompanying Document, WSB 20 Winery Record (optional use), and WSB 21 and 21B Production Declaration. WSB 13 Vineyard Register form is for new vineyards, but sections two and three must be completed if any changes have been made to the vineyard area.

Hiring pickers

All pickers over the age of 25, even those from outside the EU, are entitled to the National Living Wage of £7.50 (as of April 2017). Pickers aged 18–20 are entitled to £5.60 an hour and those aged 21–24 are entitled to £7.05 an hour. This applies to part-timers, casual or day labourers, as well as agency workers, and if you use an agency it is your responsibility to ensure that it is licenced by the Gangmasters' Licensing Authority.

As well as their living wage entitlement, part-time, casual and agency pickers have the same health and safety rights as any other worker. All staff should be briefed on company procedures in case of accidents as well as where the accident book is kept and what paperwork should be completed in case of injury. There should be enough first-aiders, properly trained and equipped, to deal with minor injuries – especially wasp stings!

Other harvest considerations include the hire and maintenance of sufficient portable lavatories for pickers, crates of a size that pickers can lift when full without risk of injury, adequate insurance and timesheets/employee forms for the pickers.

The Guide for Workers & Employers, explaining worker categories, sick pay and working time regulations etc. can be found online at **www.hse.gov.uk/workers/employers.htm**.

Legal advice

Legal assistance is available for UK winegrowers from APP Wine Law **www.appwinelaw.com**, which advises and assists with both UK and EU laws and regulations governing the production, labelling and marketing of wine, the sale and distribution of wine in the UK and abroad, mail order and online selling and conditions of sale and supply; also agreements with commercial agents, distributors and joint venture partners for the UK and abroad, supply agreements with retailers (including the Groceries Supply Code of Practice), bottling contracts (and other wine-related commercial agreements and documents), and protection and licensing of intellectual property rights in relation to wine products and brands.

Wines of Great Britain (WineGB) is the national association for the English and Welsh wine industry. WineGB's mission is to advance the multiple interests of all its members to establish Great Britain as one of the world's great quality wine regions. WineGB was formed on 1st September 2017 from the merger of the United Kingdom Vineyards Association (UKVA) and English Wine Producers (EWP). The merger brought together the resources, skills and expertise of both organisations to form a single and effective industry body.

Grape growing and winemaking in the UK has changed dramatically over the last decades. England and Wales now have over 2,500 hectares under vine, with around 700 vineyards (not all commercial) and over 160 wineries, producing an average of 6m bottles. The wines produced encompass sparkling and still white, rosé and red wines, and many of them widely acclaimed through successes in blind tastings and competitions as well as numerous accolades in the media both here and overseas.

The rate of growth that this industry has seen, and continues to experience, is exponential; in the last ten years hectarage under vine has doubled and has tripled since 2000. Earlier in 2018 WineGB commissioned an industry wide survey to provide a benchmark of where the industry currently sits and as this becomes an annual project will illustrate how it is growing and developing. Research in to how other wine regions have evolved and comparing the UK with their growth provides a framework of how the UK wine industry might expand over the next two decades. This has enabled WineGB to project 40m bottle production by 2020, with a value of £1bn; the UK wine industry shows promise of playing a significant part in this nation's agriculture as well as major contributor to employment, the rural economy, tourism and exports. For these reasons, WineGB is driving greater dialogue with all levels of Government to outline the support that is now needed to stimulate a profitable and sustainable industry

WineGB is dedicated to ensuring that viable future for the UK wine industry by:

- Providing a wide range of services, technical expertise, guidance and benefits to all its members
- Bringing a clear and powerful voice to campaign across all levels of government to secure more support for this growing sector, from Whitehall to local authorities and other associated bodies to access support on tourism, planning and economic development
- Developing training and education across all skills within the industry; from new entrants to upskilling opportunities for all members
- Fostering growth and investment, and encouraging new entrants into the market and help expand businesses over the long-term
- Promoting and supporting the industry and its wines through extensive generic marketing opportunities, its website and through social media

WineGB membership already represents the vast majority of the industry. There are various levels of membership open to growers, producers, consultants, trade, students and interested individuals.

For more information on membership and how to join, please visit www.winegb.co.uk or contact WineGB's Head Office on Tel: 01858 467792 or email office@winegb.co.uk

www.winegb.co.uk

Chapter Four
Winemaking

Case Studies

Three-quarters of the UK's 522 (2017 figure from Food Standards Agency) commercial grape-growers don't make their own wine. They either sell their fruit to one of the 133 that do, or send it to a contract winemaker to be expertly vinified and packaged. There are sound commercial reasons why so many growers aren't winemakers too; a winery is both a large additional investment and, given the many and varied compliances involved, can at times be difficult to run.

Nevertheless, the further down the processing route you can take your product, the more of the (potential) profit stays in the business, and for that reason among others (not least that being a winemaker seems incredibly romantic – from a distance, anyway!) many newcomers to the industry either start with or plan to add, when they can, a winery of their own.

Of all the weighty matters to consider at the very outset, perhaps the most important – because it will be almost irreversible – is what sort of wine you plan to make. Sparkling wine and still wine require very different winery equipment, as do red, white and rosé. They require a wide spread of grape varieties, too, which tend to have calendars and therefore labour requirements of their own, which in turn will affect the cash flow projections in your business plan.

You also need to think about the total tonnage of each variety you can reasonably expect to harvest each year. How many vines of each variety should you plant? Will they be ready at the same time? Can they be processed together or should you make separate lots from each batch? Should you bottle them separately or blend them together? These decisions will determine the capacity of the press you install and the number and volume of the tanks you will need for fermentation and subsequent blending.

If you have bought an existing vineyard your options will be limited by the varieties already planted. But even if you have planted your own vines you will be restricted in exactly the same way by the choices you make right now. So make the right ones!

Becoming a licensed wine producer

If you intend to sell any of your wine you will need to be licensed as a Wine Producer. This means that all the wine you produce will be subject to duty at the prevailing rate. If you are only producing for personal consumption and do not intend to sell or trade the wine for money or any other consideration (this can be assumed to mean bartering), then you do not need to register and become licensed, and you will not be liable for duty. In theory! Actually, producing more than one family can be realistically expected to drink in one year will raise a few questions and prompt an investigation by HMRC, so you must keep records that account for each and every bottle you've produced and where it went. Notice 163 on **www.gov.uk/government/publications/excise-notice-163-wine-production** is the guidance for a Licensed Wine Producer – it is a dry read, but spells out the obligations that go with producing wine. See Appendix I for a précis.

The duty rates change nearly every year at the Chancellor's Budget, but as of March 2017 wine removed from bonded warehouses is subject to the duty charges shown on the facing page (on top of which VAT at 20 per cent will also be charged).

Duty on wine and other alcohol is a very lucrative tax for any government and relatively easy to collect, so if you haven't already had a visit from the Excise officers – you will.

If you make wine and sell it commercially you are allowed to keep a certain amount back for domestic consumption by the company (the sole trader, partners or directors of a limited company), employees and guests. The actual amount allowed is determined by the previous year's production, so in your first year of commercial production you will not be entitled to any duty-free product. Once you are established with a track record of one year, the volumes you are allowed to keep for consumption by yourself and your employees is as follows:

A) 5.5 hectolitres (hectolitre = 100 litres) maximum, plus

B) 10 per cent of the production over 5.5hl

A) and B) must not exceed 11hl in total, and neither can the

Duty Rates current as of October 2018

Type of Wine	£ per 100 litres
Still wine and made-wine: exceeding 5.5 per cent - not exceeding 15 per cent ABV	£288.65 or £2.16 for 75cl bottle
Wine and made-wine: exceeding 15 per cent - not exceeding 22 per cent ABV	£384.82 or £2.89 for 75cl bottle
Sparkling wine and made-wine: exceeding 5.5 per cent - less than 8.5 per cent ABV	£279.46 or £2.10 for 75cl bottle
Sparkling wine and made-wine: 8.5 per cent and above - not exceeding 15 per cent ABV	£369.72 or £2.77 for 75cl bottle

entitlement be more than the total of the previous year's production. You must record all wine for domestic consumption clearly in your business records before removing the stock from the bonded premises.

Whether you have a vineyard, a winery or both, you will be required to submit a Production Declaration (FSA WSB21) to the Food Standards Agency by 15 January of the following year. This is a declaration of how many tonnes of grapes were produced by each vineyard and the volume of juice extracted. These forms will either be sent to registered vineyards and wineries or they are available on the Food Standards agency website, **www.food.gov.uk/business-industry/winestandards/winestandards-resources**.

Case study
Contract winemaking — Hattingley Valley Winery, Hampshire
www.hattingleyvalley.co.uk

The location of Hattingley Valley Winery in Lower Wield, Hampshire, offered owner Simon Robinson a golden opportunity to develop a state-of-the-art winery for his own production alongside a dedicated contract winemaking operation.

Wield Yard is in a very rural hamlet where planning permission for a new light industrial processing plant would be unheard of. But when Simon bought the Yard it was already established as a light industrial site with several businesses operating on it. The existing complex had to be almost entirely demolished, consisting as it did of old poultry sheds that had been roughly converted into a joinery workshop and car repair shop. The new buildings are in the vernacular style of brick and flint with oak cladding.

Originally the winery was designed to cater for the Hattingley Valley Vineyard, which has 18 acres planted with the three classic sparkling varieties, with surplus units rented out to local businesses. Demand for contract winemaking services soon became very apparent, though, and the winery expanded into the remaining units. The first harvest in 2010 saw predominantly contract winemaking, and 2011 saw production double, with extra contracts and increased yield from Hattingley's own fruit. Increased demand for Hattingley Valley's own production clients has grown the winery ten-fold to 450 tonnes capacity.

The model works very well for a well-capitalised start-up. The winery needs a press and tanks and other infrastructure for its own production. This equipment sits idle for most of the year, so it makes sense to work it as hard as possible in the short window of opportunity. There is a downside in that the initial capital investment has to take account of the extra tanks and barrels required, which also takes up space that can't be rented out to other businesses. But the advantages to the client – no outlay on equipment or premises, and no bureaucracy to worry about – means that good contractors soon find their investment has been well worth it.

Hattingley is reducing its contract services in order to increase production of its own labels, thanks to a vibrant export market and success in the domestic market. Hattingley is now actively looking for growers to supply grapes for its own production of sparkling wine.

There are four presses, a Coquard four tonne Champagne press, two 4 tonne Magnum presses for whole-bunch pressing of sparkling wine grapes plus a 1.2-tonne Magnum press that will happily cope with the smaller loads of sparkling and still grapes, either whole-bunch or crushed and de-stemmed. Temperature-controlled tanks of various types suit the individual needs of each client, and are all serviced by the in-line inert gas supply so that the team can move wine around the winery with minimal risk of oxidation. The choice of nitrogen or carbon dioxide to flush tanks and hoses from an integral system is possibly unique within the UK.

Sustainability

The winery is partly powered by photovoltaic panels on the roof of the buildings – Hattingley Valley was the first winery in the UK to do this, although one or two others have now followed suit. The winery also uses lighter-weight bottles to reduce the carbon footprint of the production further. In addition, there is a state-of-the-art Bio-Bubble wastewater digestor that processes all the winery wastewater. The result is that the effluent from the winery is treated and only water good enough to drink is actually released from the system.

Contract winemaking

You may decide that building your own winery is not a feasible option for you. There are now quite a few contract winemaking operations within the UK for both still and sparkling wines. Most of these are existing wineries with their own vineyards and production who have excess tank capacity that they wish to use to make extra money. More recently one or two wineries have been established with the express purpose of offering contract winemaking facilities. When deciding on the best contract winery for your purposes there are several crucial factors that you must consider:

Location

How far away is the winery? Not only do you have to think about how long it will take to transport the grapes from your vineyard, but what time of day you will be doing the journey. If it takes your pickers all day to harvest a full load you don't want to be setting off from Cornwall at 6:00pm to get to Kent! The winery will not thank you for turning up at midnight expecting to be unloaded. The alternative is to store the grapes overnight and set off in the morning, but unless the winery can guarantee processing the fruit that day, the grapes could end up having been picked for 24 hours or more before they get into the winery.

This can be managed (at least in the UK we don't have to worry about extreme heat at harvest time), but if the grapes are left in the sunshine or out in the vineyard there is a risk of damage from them getting too hot; if it's rainy and mild, you could get rot in the picking crates; and at the other extreme a hard frost could damage the grapes.

Planning transport for large loads of grapes (four tonnes plus) is difficult, mainly because you won't know exactly when you will be picking until a few days before you do so. You also need to allow a margin of error when calculating how long the pickers will take to harvest the fruit. A good, experienced picker can be expected to pick 400kg a day, but that is assuming a full day with no disruptions. Hauliers will have limited driving times, and if they are hanging around waiting to be loaded this will eat into their working day. You need to make sure you are ready for them when they arrive and get them on their way as fast as possible.

A good contract winemaker will work with you and possibly recommend a reliable haulier who has worked with grapes in the past. They will also give guidance on how the grapes are to be transported and what times they will accept them. Smaller loads can be delivered in a self drive hire truck or on a trailer that you drive to the winery yourself. When hiring a seven-tonne truck remember this is not the weight of the load, but combined with the weight of the truck – you can usually get three to four tonnes total weight of grapes/load.

The Food Standards Agency requires records to be kept of all grape movements across the country, so it can keep track for labelling regulations. By law, a Commercial Accompanying Document (CAD) has to travel with the grapes – you can download this from **https:// acss.food.gov.uk/sites/default/files/multimedia/pdfs/wsb15.pdf**

The winemaker

It is vital that you meet the winemaker who will be responsible for your wines and visit the winery into which you will be entrusting your year's work. Where possible try to taste something that they have made in a similar style to your requirements. It is important that you get on well with the team who will be making your wine – do they have a similar outlook regarding quality?

When inspecting a contract winery look hard for good or bad signs. How clean is it? What state is the equipment in? Ask to look in the tanks, look at the state of the pumps, the hoses and the fittings; check out the drains and the state of the floor behind and under the tanks. A well-looked after and clean winery will give you some insight into how careful the winemaking team is in general. Lack of pride in the working environment might be a sign of the care they will take over their winemaking.

Another thing to take into consideration is the number and volume of the winery's tanks. If it's equipped with lots of big tanks, how flexible is it? Will it mix your grapes and your juice with others to make up full tanks? How sure can you be that it's making separate wines out of each client's fruit? It is not unheard of for wineries to take in grapes from lots of small growers, combine them in the tank and then send back proportional amounts from the overall crop. No winery would do this without getting permission from the grower, but it is worth asking if it does happen. And make your views, either way, on this practice known to the winemaker.

The equipment

It doesn't matter how well you get on with the winemaking team or how conveniently close the winery is to your vineyard – if it doesn't have the equipment necessary to make your preferred style of wine then you have to look elsewhere. For example, if you want your top-quality Bacchus grapes to be made into an aromatic still wine, they will need to be fermented at low temperature to retain their fresh, aromatic elements. Therefore the winery must be able to regulate temperature during fermentation to get the desired results.

Conversely if you want to barrel-ferment Chardonnay or Pinot Noir then the winery has to be able to handle barrel work – does it have the equipment for this? Look not only for the barrels themselves, but also barrel racks, suitable cleaning equipment, cooper's tools to maintain the barrels and all the other accessories and accoutrements required.

If you are aiming for top quality, bottle-fermented sparkling wines the winery will need to have cold-stabilisation kit, filtration suitable for sparkling wines, a dedicated area for lees-ageing (preferably temperature-controlled), specialist equipment for riddling and disgorging, as well as labelling, foiling and packaging equipment. Also, how will they bottle your sparkling wine? A lot of sparkling wineries use mobile bottling lines from France, such as those from the Institut Oenologique de Champagne (IOC), which is a cost- and space-effective alternative to maintaining their own bottling line.

However this means that bottling is restricted to a few days each year – will that timetable suit your needs in terms of ageing your wine? For example, if you plan on only lees-ageing your wine for the minimum nine months, with the aim of releasing it within a year, you will want your wine to be bottled earlier than the mobile lines might be able to schedule. Ask the winemaker how they manage this. They may have capability to bottle small runs by hand.

For still wines the bottling can be even more crucial. For small volumes, a manual bottling line is adequate, in fact you would be hard-pushed to find an automatic bottling line for very small volumes. But if a winery makes both still and sparkling wine on the same site, you need to ask some hard questions about bottling. It is not advisable to bottle still wines on the same equipment used for sparkling wines. Although people do, it is such a risk to the quality of the still wines that it should be avoided at all costs. Still wines are normally sterile-filtered before bottling to ensure they are microbiologically stable. Sparkling wines on the other hand are only coarse-filtered because the bottling process or tirage actively encourages a healthy yeast population by introducing sugar and yeast into the bottle.

If a still wine goes into bottle with any residual sugar (either remaining from the fermentation or introduced to make a medium or sweet style) and comes into contact with yeast, there is a risk that a second fermentation will start in bottle. Not only is this a quality issue – the wine is not supposed to be sparkling – but also a safety one. Normal wine bottles are not designed to withstand the pressure of a second fermentation and will explode. Even if you discover the problem before the wines are sent out to market, the cost implication of emptying each bottle, re-filtering and re-bottling with new bottles is massive. There might also be a legal issue with excessive alcohol through the extra sugar having fermented.

Flexibility

It is worth asking if the winery will undertake only certain parts of the process on your behalf. This is particularly relevant to sparkling wine. You might decide to invest in a riddling and disgorging line on your own premises, especially if you have ample storage suitable for your sparkling wine. Some wineries insist on undertaking all stages of the processes, but others will be more amenable. Likewise, you may be able to make and bottle the wine but not have the space or capital to invest in the final stage. Contract disgorging is riddled with potential problems. The winemaker has no idea of the history of the wine and how well the tirage and secondary fermentation went. Upon disgorging he or she might find an insufficiency or surfeit of pressure, causing excessive loss of wine. The wine might be unstable and cause the wine to foam too much to allow disgorging to take place. Be prepared for the winery rejecting a disgorging contract if they feel they won't be able to do it properly. It happens, and the client is left with having to pay again to collect wine that is no closer to being saleable. This is not the fault of the contract winemaker – it will be the fault of the initial winemaker, i.e. you.

Record-keeping

By law, all wineries have to keep strict records of where their grapes come from, the weight received, the yield of juice extracted and the number of bottles produced. See later in this chapter for more details about exactly what should be recorded and how. Ask the winemaker how they maintain these records, and if possible have a look. The records don't have to be digital (only the larger wineries in the UK are fully computerised when it comes to their records, but they do have to adhere to Food Standards Agency requirements.

The same applies to traceability and quality control. Each wine should have full records of all inputs of additives such as yeast, sugar, nutrient, etc., along with lot numbers and rates of addition. If you are ever in the unfortunate position of having to recall a product, the first thing you will need to provide to the authorities is a full traceability report – make sure that the winery can back you up with this.

The Food Standards Agency provides a template winery record (FSA WSB20) that all wineries should use – however, for contract winemaking, with grapes coming in from all over and possibly being blended, this form is not fit for purpose. Many wineries use it for guidance, but maintain their own system either on paper or with specialist winery software.

Insurance

Having your own insurance against loss through accident or negligence is vital when undergoing contract winemaking. The winery itself should have their own insurance to cover such eventualities, but it will be limited. If you want to insure for the final value of your wine, rather than just the cost, that will remain your responsibility. Accidents do happen in wineries: it is inevitable at some point that a tank valve will fail, the press could break down with your grapes inside, or the bottling line might malfunction. It won't necessarily be anyone's fault, but the outcome can be financially disastrous, especially for a small producer who has limited stock in the first instance.

VAT on winemaking services

Services supplied within a tax or bonded warehouse can be taxed at the standard 20 per cent VAT rate or they can be zero-rated if the customer prefers (e.g. if they are not VAT-registered), provided the services are in relation to making a new product – this applies to winemaking; the initial product, grapes, becomes a completely different product while in the tax warehouse (the winery) so VAT never becomes liable. The customer needs to supply the contract winemaker (or tax warehousekeeper) with a certificate requesting this zero-rating, and any invoices must show VAT applied to the services as 'zero-rated'. For full details see Notice 702/10 at **www.hmrc.gov.uk**.

Making your final choice

Once you have shortlisted your contract wineries of choice you could ask for testimonials from other happy clients. The UK wine industry is small and tight-knit, there are very few secrets amongst us all! The winery should be able to provide contact details of existing clients who can vouch for the service they have received.

There are others who do contract winemaking on an ad-hoc basis – if you have a winery nearby it would be worth asking if they would consider taking on a contract client.

Some wineries offering contract winemaking services

Bolney Wine Estate
Foxhole Lane, Bolney, Haywards Heath, RH17 5NB
Tel: +44 (0)1444 881575
www.bolneywineestate.com

Hattingley Valley Winery
Wield Yard, Lower Wield, Alresford, Hampshire, SO24 9RX,
Tel: +44 (0)1256 389188
www.hattingleyvalley.co.uk

Litmus Wines, London Road, Dorking, Surrey RH5 6AA
Tel: +44 (0)1306 879829
www.litmuswines.com

Stanlake Park, Twyford, Berkshire, RG10 0BN
Tel: +44 (0)118 9340176
www.stanlakepark.com

Three Choirs Vineyard Estate
Newent, Gloucestershire, GL18 1LS
Tel: +44 (0)1531 890223
www.three-choirs-vineyards.co.uk

Vivid Wines
New House Winery, Mountfield, Robertsbridge, East Sussex, TN32 5JP
Tel: +44 (0)1580 881011
www.vivid-wines.com

Wiston Estate Winery
North Farm, Washington, West Sussex, RH20 4BB,
Tel: +44 (0)1903 877845
www.wistonestate.co.uk

Case study
Converting a building — Wiston Estate Winery, West Sussex
www.wistonestate.com

Harry and Pip Goring are the current incumbents of the 6,000 acre Wiston Estate in West Sussex. Harry's family has been in residence for nearly 400 years, farming the land and running the wider estate. It was Pip's dream to plant a vineyard, having grown up surrounded by vines in her native South Africa. They enlisted the help of Dermot Sugrue who in 2006 was working at Nyetimber Vineyard, also in West Sussex. Dermot left Nyetimber to concentrate on the Wiston project shortly afterwards, planting around 20 acres of the classic Champagne varieties: Pinot Noir, Pinot Meunier and Chardonnay.

By 2008 the vines were starting to mature and the fruit was either going to have to be sold, vinified under contract elsewhere or fermented on the estate. An old turkey-processing plant was a brave choice as a winery, but Dermot saw its potential as a state-of-the-art facility. The Gorings were persuaded and gave the go-ahead to convert the old building.

Converting an existing building does have its drawbacks. Ceiling heights are fixed, drainage is not easy to retrofit and power supplies may be restricted. Being a former turkey-processing plant did have some advantages, though: power was already installed and of decent supply; the drains were in place (most were filled in but could be restored); access for large trucks from the nearby A24 was easy; and the heavily insulated rooms for chilled storage were perfect for controlling the second fermentation in bottle, if a little awkward to access.

A feature of the winery is the refurbished Coquard basket press which produces very high-quality juice but is hard work to operate and takes longer than most modern wine presses. In addition to the basket press the winery has two modern bladder presses to cope with the influx of fruit at harvest. This extra processing capacity has become vital, as the winery not only processes its own fruit but also makes wine for numerous contract clients from across the UK.

Building your own winery

If you decide that you need and/or want your own winery then you need to be prepared for considerable expense. Even if you have an existing building it is unlikely to be ready to receive grapes without adaptation.

First things first, do you need planning permission? Well, perhaps not. If you're only planning on vinifying your own grapes, grown on your own vineyard, then you are likely to fall under permitted development right, as the winery will be a necessary extension of your agricultural activities. And just as a dairy farm needs a dairy to process the milk its cows produce, so you are allowed to have a processing facility for your crop.

But wineries and vineyards are still relatively rare in the UK, and some planning authorities may not understand what it is you are doing. You may come up against a planning officer who considers winemaking and a winery as light industrial use rather than agricultural. And he or she may be quite right; making wine is an industrial process, and if you are bringing in grapes from elsewhere and/or offering contract winemaking services to third parties, then you will indeed fall into the light industrial bracket and will have to go through the whole planning process. It shouldn't actually be that onerous, and more details of how to successfully steer a planning application are given in Appendix II.

Once you have established your planning requirements, you need to think about the location of your winery. If you have a suitable existing building then this won't be a problem, but if it is in such a position as to make it impractical as a winery, then you may find yourself having to build from scratch elsewhere. A winery needs to have certain services and utilities available, so no matter how pretty your stone barn in the middle of a field may be, if you can't get sufficient water, power and drainage out to it, then it is no more than a pretty barn. And laying power cables, phone lines, water, etc., can be very expensive and may even require separate planning permissions.

Access

This is a vital element of design that can be overlooked. How will big articulated trucks carrying equipment, bottles, tanks, barrels, etc., get to your winery? What are the country lanes like around you? Often, owner-operated trucks will not want to scratch or damage the roof of their very expensive lorry on low-hanging trees. Are there any low bridges en route to your winery? And once they arrive can they turn round? Will there be room to unload from them? Is there hard-standing outside the winery or is there a risk of them getting stuck in wet weather?

Water

It is often said that it takes 10 litres of water to make one litre of wine. This is not far from the truth, although in the UK, where we don't irrigate the vines, the reality is probably closer to seven or eight litres. Do not underestimate how much water you will need, though, especially at harvest time. Winemaking is 90 per cent cleaning, and you need water, hot and cold, to do so. Sparkling wineries, when up to full production, will use even more as the riddling and disgorging schedule runs 12 months of the year.

Water used in a winery should ideally be de-chlorinated. Ordinary tap water can be used for cleaning (not ideal practice); however, additions made to the wine itself should be made with dechlorinated water. Chlorine is a trigger for 2,4,6-trichloroanisole, otherwise known as cork taint – although you don't need a cork to get TCA! Screw-capped wines that have never seen a cork can and do get contaminated in wineries where hygiene is lax, or where chlorine bleach is found in the cleaning solutions. Good practice is to have carbon filter cartridges on each tap. They are easy to access and replace.

On the following page is a table used for a 100,000-litre winery, based on a California still wine operation with modifications for the UK. The figures are huge, but don't be tempted to disbelieve them, and of course, remember that what goes in must come out, which leads us on to drainage and sewerage.

Information taken from *Winery Utilities, Planning, Design and Operation* David R. Storm KA/PP 2001

Estimated Annual Water Usage (litres) for a 100,000 litre Winery: 700,000 litres
(11,000 cases wine)

Breakdown of Usage	litres
Peak Month	84,000
Peak Month Daily Use	3,230
Peak Month Hourly Use	323
Per/min peak use	5
Per/min average use	

Typical Monthly Water Usage Distribution

Month	% of annual use	Comments
January	6	general operations
February	9	filtration
March	7	general operations
April	8	bottling
May	8	bottling
June	7	general operations
July	7	general operations
August	7	general operations
September	10	**Pre-crush cleaning**
October	12	**Harvest operations**
November	11	**Harvest operations and post-crush cleaning**
December	8	general operations
Total	100	

Hot Water for Cleaning
Examples

	L/min	Pressure/bar	Temp	Usage
Hot Water Hose Stations	25	3.50	60-70°C	Cleaning equipment/tanks/floor – sporadic usage – peak usage Eg: cleaning a tank with a caustic/rinse/citric acid/rinse cycle would take 840 litres of water (210L of which would be hot)

Cleaning the press might take 1 hour, using 1500 litres of water
Not necessarily all hot water but possible

Bottling line preparation   May use 1250 litres per cleaning, maybe twice per day

Water Usage table for 100,000-litre winery

Drainage

This is another element that is often overlooked or not truly understood when planning a winery. There are quite a few wineries in the UK that have a pervading whiff of rotten eggs and other nasties at busy periods. This is because the drainage facilities are inadequate for the size and type of processing plant. While you are using a lot of water, you will also be sending an awful lot of chemical cleaning agents and solid matter from the grapes into the drainage system. If you are in an urban area, mains drainage may well take care of it, especially if you are on an industrial estate; but the Environment Agency will still take an interest, especially in a more rural area.

Winery wastewater has little or no oxygen and is therefore toxic to plant and water life. It has a high solid content and very low pH because of the acidic nature of grapes, juice and wine. The fermentation process uses up most of the bio-nutrients in the wastewater, leaving it deficient and unable to break down untreated. There are various options for treating the wastewater. One of these, proving quite popular where tourism is a possibility, is the creation of a wetland for wildlife. In Australia, New Zealand and other wine-producing countries, these reedbeds and wetlands become tourist attractions in themselves. An alternative is a series of settling tanks that will allow the solids to settle out, with clear water running out at the end. This is probably the easiest and cheapest to install, but the downside is that it will need to be emptied occasionally, and the water that is released into the storm drains, or water table, may not meet Environment Agency criteria.

The method that is probably the best option for a UK winery, with relatively low maintenance (unlike a reedbed system), is an aerobic digester. A big tank is sunk into the ground below the winery and all run-off, solids, winery waste, sanitary waste and greywater is drained into it. The bacteria in the digester get to work on the sewage, consuming the solid matter and releasing water clean enough to be returned to the water table. With a winery being seasonal in operation, the biggest problem is keeping the bacteria fed and healthy during the quiet times.

Wineries usually have a large expanse of roof that can be utilised for rainwater harvesting. This 'greywater' can be treated and used within the winery for cleaning floors and flushing toilets. The water can be treated by ultra violet (UV) to ensure any bacteria are killed. In the UK, unlike California or Australia for example, we are not so restricted on our water use and it is not expensive. However, beware the cost of the treatment and pumping equipment required to re-use rainwater – it might take a few decades to realise any financial saving. Environment Agency Greywater information can be found at:
www.gov.uk/government/publications/energy-and-carbon-implications-of-rainwater-harvesting-and-greywater-recycling

Other resources include:
Create an Oasis with Greywater, Art Ludwig.
Harvesting rainwater for domestic uses: an information Guide,
Environment Agency.
*Reclaimed Water Systems; Information About Installing, Modifying or
Maintaining Reclaimed Water Systems*, WRAS Information and Guidance
note, *August No. 9-02-04* **www.wras.co.uk.**
UK Rainwater Harvesting Association **www.ukrha.org.**

Flooring

Integral to the drainage is the flooring. The floors should ideally
have a 3 per cent gradient towards the drains to ensure quick and
complete drainage. Wine has a very low pH that will corrode most
flooring materials, even concrete. On the other hand the caustic
soda used in most cleaning fluids has a very high pH and is equally corrosive. Your decision on flooring is one you will live with for
a long time so whatever you choose, keep contact time with all
these corrosive liquids as short as possible! There are many options and they all have a price tag according to how multi-purpose
they are.

Polished, power-floated concrete is cheap, easy to apply and
doesn't require specialist contractors. However, it is corroded by
prolonged contact with wine and chemicals, and is very slippery
when wet (which it will be most of the time), so not good for
health and safety. Concrete is also porous so can be a haven for
bacteria – and a thin layer of protective coating won't withstand
much heavy work before cracking or wearing out.

Epoxy resin is a relatively cheap and durable flooring, but it's
not very resistant to thermal shock; the resin layer often comes
away from the base concrete under extremes of temperature. It is
relatively innocuous while being applied, and can be re-applied
while the winery is in use if necessary. It is laid in one continuous
go and trowelled by hand, so seams are less of an issue, but it can
crack under extreme weight (such as forklifts).

Polyurethane: is the most versatile flooring and also one of the most expensive, depending on how thick it is laid. It is resistant to thermal shock and chemical spillage, and is easy to clean because it is laid in one go (trowelled on by hand) so has no seams. It cures faster than epoxy (in under 12 hours) and the odour is not detrimental to the wine if it is laid retrospectively. Both epoxy and polyurethane can have aggregate added to the mix to increase the slip resistance, but this does make them both slightly harder to clean.

Methyl Methacrylate (MMA): sets very fast (in less than an hour in some cases), is resistant to thermal shock and chemicals, durable and often cheaper than polyurethane. It is used in food-processing plants and in some wine facilities, but there is concern that the odours it gives off when freshly laid can damage the wine. If you are re-laying an existing winery floor or will be using the winery very shortly after the floor goes down, you should avoid MMA. But if you are doing the work long before any grapes or wine are introduced, you could consider it.

Power

The amount of power required for a commercial winery can be a surprise, and most of it will stand idle during the year. However, at harvest, when you are running a press, de-stemmer, crusher, temperature control, pumps, etc., all at the same time, you will soon see the need for what might seem like an excessive power supply. Most of these big consumers of power will need a 20-amp fuse dedicated to them. A 100-amp capacity is not over the top for a commercial winery, but you will need to tailor it to your individual needs.

Most wineries run on three-phase power. French equipment often comes fitted with 4-pin three-phase plugs, while most UK power points will be 5-pin for three-phase. You can either request your electrician uses 4-pin (if most of your kit will be coming from France) or keep a supply of extension leads and converters to hand.

Wineries are by their very nature wet places, with juice, water and wine all being splashed around pretty freely. It is vital that your power points and plugs are the highest waterproof grade you can afford. Good maintenance of your plugs, power points and electricity supply is mandatory for all businesses in the UK under the Health and Safety at Work Act 1974 (HSWA), and more specifically the Provision and Use of Work Equipment Regulation 1998 (PUWER). You can use a contractor to check your plugs through the Portable Appliance Testing scheme. Even if you do use a contractor and get your PAT certificate annually, you must also regularly check the integrity of your fittings and leads, especially during and after busy periods.

It is impossible to say what level of power your winery will need without knowing the projected level of production. When looking at equipment (it is a good idea to start looking long before you break ground for the winery itself) always make a note of the power needs. This will help you plan your power requirement. Any good electrician will be able to look at the power needs of all the kit you will be running, taking into account how much of it will be run simultaneously, and work out how much power you will need. Most commercial wineries are unlikely to need more than a 100-amp power supply, but think about your potential growth.

Communications

Being a winemaker and vine-grower can be isolating in the best possible way, but your business cannot be an island: you will need internet access, a landline and mobile phone reception. If telephone cables are not already laid to the winery site you will need to get them installed. Likewise, broadband internet connections are not a given in rural areas (although it is getting better), and if you are too far from an exchange you might not be able to access mainstream broadband. If you are going to run your internet sales from the winery, you need to have reliable and fast broadband access.

Access to orders from the website and emails from customers demand rapid responses. You need a back-up option for internet access to ensure you keep on top of this side of things, and there are few companies that offer private broadband access to rural areas via a series of wireless receivers. These can be very good, with far faster speeds than the standard, but are more susceptible to interference and are generally much more expensive.

Handling equipment

Handling the grapes is a trickier business and requires more space and equipment than you might have thought. The tractor trundles into the yard pulling a trailer laden with overflowing crates that have to be unloaded by hand, pallet-truck or forklift, in an area just outside the winery, preferably under cover, where you can weigh the grapes. If you are unloading on pallets then you need a weigh scale that can take the weight of a full pallet. A pallet truck that can also weigh is a very useful tool because it can perform more than one job. The alternative is a platform scale loaded by forklift.

If you are going to use small crates coming straight from the vineyard for whole bunch pressing, then consider how they are going to be unloaded and carried into the winery. Champagne-style picking crates holding nearly 50kg of grapes are not uncommon but take two people to handle when full. It is much better to go for 20kg crates or even smaller, which can be handled safely by a single worker. The crates should ideally be vented on at least two sides and the bottom, so the grapes don't sit in their own juice or water while waiting to be transferred to the winery. Also, think about where and how you are going to wash the crates, which has to be done immediately after unloading. Sticky grape juice left for more than a couple of hours is more difficult to rinse off than you would ever believe! A dedicated crate-washer is the best option (although expensive), but a powerful hose or jet-washer on tarmac or hard-standing can do the job – it will just take longer and you will get much wetter while doing it.

Wherever you do the weighing will require a flat surface, preferably under cover and with plenty of room for manoeuvre. The scales need to be well maintained and should be calibrated every year. Your winery records and yield of wine will be based on the receival weight. If you are weighing heavy, and then don't get the yield of juice you should from the stated weight, the Wine Standards Board and possibly HMRC will be asking where the missing wine (and therefore duty revenue) has gone.

Forklift types

There are three types of forklift: electric, gas and diesel. Which one you choose will be dependent on a number of factors. Will it be working outside in the rain? Will you be working only outside? Will it need to be operated inside the winery? The pros and cons of each type are detailed below for consideration.

Your next consideration is the weight you have to lift and therefore the rated capacity of the forklift. A stillage cage filled with 500 bottles of sparkling wine can weigh close to a tonne, while a load of grapes will probably not get much above 500kg. How high do you want to lift such a weight? Do you want a side shift for ease of stacking cages, or would a tipping mechanism be better for loading grapes into the press?

Type	Pros	Cons
Electric	Quiet to use No emissions or fumes Can be used inside safely Easy to refuel on-site	Expensive to buy Requires a charging station Cannot be operated safely in rain Can take more than eight hours to charge
Gas	Cheaper to buy Lower emissions and fumes than diesel Can be used inside with ventilation Can be used outside in the rain Quick and easy to refuel	Noisy Heavy gas canisters to change Must have a spare canister at all times Emit fumes so can be smelly indoors
Diesel	Cheap to buy Easy to refuel Can be used outside in the rain	Noisy and dirty Can't be used safely inside High emissions and fumes

If you visit the dealer either to buy or hire a forklift make sure you go armed with the facts about what you will be using it for. Renting a forklift on a long-term contract can be cost-effective, as the maintenance contract will usually be part of the deal. To use a forklift legally, even on your own premises, you and any staff operating it need to be certified by a recognised training body. Plumpton College offers three-day forklift courses from Lantra, but other agricultural colleges also offer these. A cheaper alternative is to hire an instructor to come on-site to your winery and train a small group on the forklift they will be using. A quick search on Google will help you locate a provider close to you.

A last word on pallet trucks: most of the different types available have very small wheels, not much bigger than castors, which really only work on mirror-smooth surfaces. They can cope with gravel but tend to get stuck on anything larger such as chippings. If you only need a pallet-truck or pump-truck, choose a model with larger wheels.

THE
MICROBREWERS'
HANDBOOK

By Ted Bruning

"A fascinating book...indispensable"
Roger Protz

FIFTH EDITION

THE
MICROBREWERS'
Ted Bruning   HANDBOOK

"Indispens... ...ed to bolt together mash tun, copper and fermenters"
Roger Protz

"Indispensable if you are tempted to bolt together mash tun, copper and fermenters"
Roger Protz

"If you are considering creating your own brewery, whatever your motivation, you should buy and read this book as your first step"
Hopmaltbrew.com

The microbrewing scene has changed beyond recognition in the eight years since the first edition of this book was published. The sheer number of small independent breweries at work, up and down the land, has now more than doubled to around 1,500.

Ted Bruning, leading beer author, guides you through the practicalities of starting your own microbrewery; from how to brew right through to finding a place of your own.

- How to source the correct equipment
- Advice on developing the necessary skills, raising the finance and finding appropriate premises
- Specialist advice on the design, promotion and marketing of your beer
- Detailed case studies of those who have started their own microbreweries with the pitfalls explained
- Directory of services and suppliers

www.posthousepublishing.com

Chapter Five

Process Equipment

You can now source all the equipment you will need to get started with from UK importers/distributors such as Vigo Ltd of Honiton in Devon, whose catalogue of vineyard, orchard, winemaking and cidermaking kit you can see at **www.vigoltd.com**. Another good source is Core Equipment at **www.core-equip.com**. Very little of the equipment is manufactured in the UK, though, so if you want to explore the full range of what's available – and if you have the time and money – then you will have to go shopping in person. Equipment fairs such as SITEVI in Montpellier, ViniTech in Bordeaux and SIMEI in Milan and Munich are usually held every year and all have websites that are easily found. If you do visit one of these events, though, don't be dazzled by all the chrome. Compatibility and compliance are vital issues, especially when buying equipment made outside the EU. Will it work in Britain? Is it legal in Britain? And are the warranties worth the paper they're written on in Britain?

Don't be over-influenced by price, either. Many British craft distillers are buying small and inexpensive handcrafted pot-stills from artisanal coppersmiths in Portugal and elsewhere; but then a pot-still has no moving parts – in fact it's really just a bucket with an upside-down funnel on top. A press, by contrast, is a highly-mechanised piece of engineering, and there's no point saving a couple of thousand Euros on a press from an obscure supplier in Slovakia if you then lose all you've saved when the press breaks down and there are no engineers on hand with the knowledge and spare parts to fix it. You could lose your entire harvest that way. Servicing and repair, especially repair at short notice, are necessary parts of the purchase, and if you're the only winery in the UK with a certain make of machinery, you'll pay through the nose to get a dedicated engineer to come to the UK to look after it for you. Either look for manufacturers who already have clients in the UK or buy/lease from an established UK supplier who can service your kit before every harvest and rush a man with a spanner out to you if things go wrong at the worst possible moment (and since you only use the machinery when you absolutely need it, every moment is the worst possible moment).

Still red wine

Grapes destined for red wine production have to be de-stemmed and crushed before fermentation can start. Red wine fermentation is carried out on the skins before pressing; all you need to do is extract the stalks and break the skins open to release the juice. In some warmer regions of the world, whole bunches are used in red wine fermentation, but this is not usually recommended for English red wines where ripeness is marginal – the stalks will be green and will cause astringency in the resulting wine.

A de-stemmer is essentially a horizontal cylinder with holes along its length. Inside the cylinder are rubber paddles that turn to push the grapes through it. The grapes fall through the holes and the stems are ejected from the end. The best-quality machines will allow you to adjust the turning speed of the paddles as well as the speed of the cylinder to allow for berries of different sizes. The berries can then be transferred directly into the fermenting vessel, or passed through a crusher.

Crushing the grapes breaks the skins to allow the juice to be released prior to fermentation. It is a good idea to get your crusher from the same supplier as your de-stemmer, to be sure that one will fit directly under the other. Transferring the crushed grapes to the fermentation vessel can be messy: a must-pump is a useful but expensive option unless you're producing a fair quantity. Smaller volumes can be bucketed.

Tanks for red wine production are subtly different to those used for white wines. Because the grapes go into the tanks more or less whole, the doors are usually positioned at the very bottom of the tank to allow the pomace to be easily removed after fermentation. Above that there's usually another opening from which the wine itself is drained off. The cap or raft of skins that floats on the top of the wine as it ferments also affects the construction and working of the red wine fermentation tank. The cap needs to be kept wet for three main reasons: to prevent the growth of bacteria in the skins; to extract more colour and other phenolics from the grapes; and to aerate the fermenting must. There are several ways of doing this – ask five winemakers which is the best method and you will get five different answers. It is often related to the grape variety and style of wine: Pinot Noir is often punched down, Cabernet Sauvignon more often pumped over, while wines needing additional oxygen during fermentation or extra extraction have liquid racked off and then poured back in. The three principle ways are:

Punching down

This is when you physically, either manually or with a pneumatic device, force the cap back under the fermenting liquid until it is completely wet and submerged. It is known as *pigeage* in French.

Pumping over

This is when you attach a hose and pump to the bottom valve of the tank and pump the liquid out and over the top of the tank, thoroughly wetting the cap. This is known as *remontage* in French.

Rack and return

This is similar to a pump over, with the addition of another vessel or tank being utilised between the tank and the pump returning to the tank to 'splash' the wine, allowing an aerative racking.

Once fermentation of the red wines has finished you will need to drain the wine from the pomace and let it settle for a few days without pump overs or punch downs. If you're storing the wine in an open vat you can sprinkle some dry ice over it to prevent oxidation; if in a closed tank, simply tighten the top to trap the existing carbon dioxide. The 'free-run' wine can then be drawn off the bottom valve.

This will be the best wine, but there is still a considerable volume within the skins and pulp. This has to pressed to extract the remaining liquid, which is known as the 'press wine'. You will need to decide whether it is good enough to mix back into the free-run wine. This will depend to an extent on how hard you press the pomace. You may decide to keep it separate and make a lesser wine for your own consumption, use it as 'topping wine' for your barrels or other vessels where a small percentage won't affect the quality or send it to a distiller to have it turned into marc or grappa.

Still white wine and sparkling base wines

Grapes intended for still white wines can either be de-stemmed and crushed before pressing, which is the fast and efficient way, or pressed in whole bunches, the method used for better-quality still whites and almost universally for sparkling wines. If you are looking at presses and you are quoted for a press size in hectolitres, they are probably talking about crushed, de-stemmed fruit capacity, whereas if you are quoted in terms of the tonnage it will accept, then it is more likely to be based on the weight of whole bunches. Make sure you understand in what terms the supplier is talking about before you commit!

Types of press

There are numerous options, but the most common types are detailed below:

Basket press

Large versions of these are used in Champagne where Coquard is the ubiquitous supplier. Essentially a large basket made of wooden or stainless steel slats with a juice tray underneath, a hydraulically operated plate is then pressed on to the top of the grapes to force the juice out through the slats into the tray. To ensure an even extraction from the grapes, the pomace needs to be manually shifted in between pressing cycles. This is often called the *retrousse* and it is a labour intensive operation, with a larger press size adding considerable time to the processing. Coquard has updated the design principle with its new PAI press that operates horizontally, eliminating the need for manual intervention during the pressing cycle. There are many other manufacturers of basket-type presses from across Europe. A visit to one of the many equipment fairs would give you the opportunity to see all the options in one go.

Bladder press or pneumatic press

These presses come in many sizes and variations. The principle of the operation is a stainless steel vat, mounted horizontally, with an air bladder inside. The air bladder is filled by a compressor, squeezing the grapes against the wall of the vat where grills allow the juice to run out. Variations on this are centrally mounted grills with a bladder either side; open-vat presses where the grills allow the juice to run down the outside of the vat and into the juice tray; or closed-vat presses with internal grills allowing the press to be operated under inert gas, releasing the juice out through channels.

If you are making only sparkling wine then an open-vat press is better – allowing some oxidation of the juice as it runs down the press – but if you are also making still white wines and pressing red wines off you might want to consider a closed-vat press that will allow you to operate the press anaerobically, or under inert gas, to retain primary fruit aromas.

Up to about 4 tonnes (whole bunch weight) a bladder press will come with its own internal air compressor and can also still be mounted on wheels. Any bigger than that and you will probably need an external reservoir of compressed air and a stand-alone compressor. And you will have to fix the press to the floor, making moving it somewhat difficult.

Horizontal screw press

This type of press is going out of fashion and is more often used in large-scale wineries where crushing and de-stemming is the norm. The operation principle is the same as the basket press, but horizontal rather than vertical – it allows for greater volumes to be processed faster than a basket press. It is mostly found in large-scale wineries.

Continuous screw press

These are now almost obsolete and you would probably only find one on the secondhand market. There is a reason for this – the quality of juice is not good. They are rough on the grapes and are actually prohibited in lots of quality wine regions.

Case study
Planting a vineyard — Tinwood Estate, West Sussex
www.tinwoodestate.com

A final year dissertation on farm diversification planted the seed of an idea in Wye College agricultural business management student Art Tukker. The form of diversification he focused on was viticulture, and his research took him to many English vineyards including Chapel Down, where Owen Elias was able to steer him in the right direction.

Art's family farmed at Tinwood near Chichester in West Sussex, and the field where the iceberg lettuces grew would, he realised, make an ideal vineyard: south-west facing, sloping, chalk under flint, two miles inland but sheltered.

Immediately after graduating from Wye in 2005 Art started his homework in earnest and spent a harvest at Huia, a small high-quality vineyard near Marlborough in New Zealand. Back home, he settled on planting the classic Champagne trio of Chardonnay, Pinot Noir and Pinot Meunier, intending to make the sparkling wines for which England was then becoming renowned. In 2006 he became one of Ridgeview Estate's supplier partners – they sourced the vines, he supplied the labour. And a fair bit of labour it was, too. In spring 2007 and 2008 he planted 84,000 vines on 50 acres, putting up 84,000 supports, 10,000 line posts and more than 500 end posts. In 2011 he planted another five acres.

After all the hard work – much of which he did himself – Art treated himself to a short course in winegrowing and winemaking at Plumpton College. In 2009 he got his first crop and gained a little more practical experience by working on the vintage at Ridgeview. Most of Tinwood's output goes to Ridgeview, but in 2012 Art started releasing small quantities of his own sparkling wines to great acclaim.

Looking after the environment has always been a key part of Tinwood Estate's role and in 2010 they entered the Entry Level Stewardship scheme. They have planted wild flower meadows, new hedgerows and now special wild flowers amongst the vines to promote biodiversity on the farm.

Hydro-presses

These are for small-scale enterprises and come in various sizes suitable for home winemaking and smaller commercial wineries. Similar in operation to a pneumatic bladder press, instead of the internal bag being blown up with compressed air the rubber bag inside the press is inflated by filling it with water. The juice then runs out of the stainless steel perforated cylinder.

Manufacturers that supply to the UK already include: Magnum de Franceschi by Oeno Concept, Epernay, France **www.oenoconcept. com**; Bucher Vaslin, Switzerland **www.buchervaslin.com**; Europress, Germany **www.scharfenberger.de**; Willmes, UK agent, Vigo Ltd **www. vigoltd.com**; SK Group, **www.sk-skrlj.com**; Bevtech **www.bevtech. co.uk**; and Core Equipment **www.core-equip.com**.

Tanks

The size and type of your tanks will depend on the size of your vineyard and the parcels within it. If you want to ferment the individual parcels separately, then you will need to get more and smaller tanks, which will increase your costs. If the intention is then to blend wines, obviously you'll need bigger tanks as well. Bear in mind the size of your press and the volumes you can expect to extract in one pressing cycle. How close together will the grapes come in? Can you add one pressing to the previous one in the tank before settling begins?

With sparkling wine, if your press will take four tonnes of whole bunches you can expect to get 2,000 litres of the best juice for your *cuvée* and about 500 litres of heavier pressings or *taille*. Will you be separating these out from one another? With sparkling wine you can generally expect a yield of approximately 50 per cent *cuvée* and 10 per cent *taille*, while with still wines you could take up to 70 per cent juice from the grapes. So, on 1,000kg, 60 per cent yield would be 600 litres. This is a decision that has to be finalised at the pressing itself, according to the quality of the fruit, the level of rot, the ripeness, etc.

White wine tanks have a door raised above the base of the tank. This allows you a settling space at the bottom for solids and, later, yeast lees from the fermentation. After draining off the bulk of the juice or wine you can open the door to carefully watch the remaining clear liquid off the solids. This is either done by the use of a racking plate, or the tank will be fitted with a racking arm that you control from outside the tank. The latter is the easiest way.

Manufacturers that supply the UK already are: Metalinox, a family-owned company from the Loire Valley, dimitri.dupaillon@metalinox-sas.fr **www.metalinox-cuves.fr**; SK Group, **www.sk-skrlj.com**; Speidel, UK agent, Vigo Ltd **www.vigoltd.com**; and Bevtech **www.bevtech.co.uk**.

Valves

The racking valve of a tank should be a ball valve to allow the insertion of equipment such as rousers or stirrers, while the bottom valve should be a butterfly valve for ease of cleaning. The fittings on these valves should all match the other equipment in the winery. DN fittings are the most common in the UK and DN40 is a manageable size. Watch out for secondhand equipment with weird and wonderfully old-fashioned fittings left over from the imperial days. Any savings you make on the kit could be lost by having to commission reducers and converters to fit your other equipment. Macon fittings are ubiquitous throughout Europe, so when ordering new kit from suppliers always specify the type and size fitting you want.

With DN fittings there is always a male and female end. It makes operations go more smoothly if all equipment such as tanks and presses and pumps are male and all hoses are female. That way you'll never find yourself with a hose with the wrong fitting. Always useful, however, are a few adaptors such as a male-to-male connector that can join two female hoses together in case extra length is needed.

Temperature control or thermo-regulation

Once your juice has been pressed you will need to settle out any solid matter. This is done either with enzymes or by cold-settling. If you are cold-settling then you need to get the juice below 10°C (enzymes, though, won't work below 12°C). So either your tanks need individually controlled thermo-regulation or you need to install them in a cold room. The former option is far more efficient.

Once you have settled the juice for 12–24 hours you will rack it off the solids into another tank and initiate fermentation. For the yeast to start fermenting in ideal conditions the juice should be at no less than 15°C. Once fermenting the temperature will depend on what style of wine you are making. An aromatic white such as Bacchus might be maintained at 15°C while a sparkling base wine, where you are not attempting to retain primary fruit aromas, can be allowed to rise to 20°C or maybe even more. A red wine being fermented on its skins will need to be kept warm and allowed to reach 30°C before cooling kicks in.

Once alcoholic fermentation has finished, the wine may need to go through malolactic fermentation, when the harsher malic acid is converted to softer lactic acid by malolactic bacteria. To enable this conversion, the wine needs to be maintained between 20 and 25°C: any hotter and the bugs will die; cooler and they become dormant.

When deciding on the extent of your thermo-regulation system you need to consider if you will require heating and cooling at the same time. This adds considerably to the cost, because you effectively need two circuits for the glycol, but it also gives you ultimate flexibility.

Two suppliers of dedicated winery thermo-regulation systems found in the UK are Vigo Ltd, sales@vigoltd.com **www.vigoltd.com** and TR Equipements, **www.trequipements.fr**.

Chaptalisation – additions to wine

There are certain additions you can make to your juice and/or wine to help nature along its way. In the UK we rarely see sugar levels in the grapes that would allow us to produce wines with a natural alcoholic volume of more than 11–12 per cent; and those wines that do reach the giddy heights of 11 per cent are from grape varieties specifically bred to ripen well in cool climates, but not necessarily of the highest quality.

The classic sparkling varieties of Chardonnay, Pinot Noir and Pinot Meunier will very seldom achieve more than 10 per cent natural potential before harvest in October, and they will also retain more acidity than would be acceptable for a still wine. For both still and sparkling wines you are permitted to add sugar (chaptalise) up to three per cent potential alcohol to the juice after pressing and before or during the primary fermentation. Potential alcohol in this context is another word for sugar, whether the natural grape sugars fructose and glucose, or sucrose courtesy of Silver Spoon or Tate & Lyle. In exceptionally cool years the WineGB can apply to the EU for an extra 0.5 per cent potential alcohol at chaptalisation.

The Wine Standards Board regulates the addition of sugar, or 'enrichment' of juice as it is known. There are minimum natural alcohol levels your juice/grapes must reach before enrichment or chaptalisation, and these differ slightly for sparkling and still wines. Essentially, the total potential alcohol level after enrichment must be at least 8.5 per cent, meaning that the absolute minimum level of ripeness of the grapes has to have been 5.5 per cent. The levels are detailed on the Wine Standards Board website where you can also download the official WSB10 Notice of Enrichment form that you are legally obliged to complete and send to your Wine Standards Inspector at least 48 hours before you carry out the enrichment operation.

Whether you measure your sugar by Brix, Baumé, Specific Gravity or Oeschle, you must ensure your conversion rates are accurate enough to satisfy the WSB requirements. For the additions you can assume that just under 17g/l of sugar will translate to one per cent potential alcohol. It is not an exact science because the conversion of sugar to ethanol during the fermentation is not always linear.

De-acidification

This is a rarely used technique even on sparkling base wines, which have some of the highest acid levels of all. The lees-ageing period for sparkling wines softens the acidity, as does malolactic fermentation. But for some aromatic still wines where MLF is not an option and the acidity levels are still high, artificial de-acidification is necessary. It's a very violent process that carries a risk of severe oxidation as the pH is significantly raised. If you have to do it at all, you should do it to the unfermented juice rather than the wine if possible. The WSB requires notification of any de-acidification operation regardless of when it takes place, and the notification does not have to be received in advance, unlike with enrichment – use Form WSB14.

There are two ways to remove acidity: single salt and double salt. Calcium carbonate will remove only tartaric acid, so if you have 7g/l total acidity and 5g/l of that is malic acid, you can remove 2g/l of acidity with calcium carbonate but you'll still be left with 5g/l of malic acid. To remove both tartaric and malic acid you need to use the double salt method. This will remove roughly 1g/l of each g/l, so you need to be aware of their respective levels in order to avoid removing all the tartaric. There are several proprietary double salt preparations each with different actions and instructions. It is best to take advice from the supplier before embarking on any de-acidification.

Cold-stabilisation

A vital stage in the process of white and sparkling winemaking. The naturally occurring potassium bitartrate (KHT) as tartaric acid in wine will often precipitate out when the wine is chilled, forming a crystalline substance in the bottle that can look worryingly like glass. It is not harmful in itself but it is considered a fault, especially by retailers who don't want to have to explain what it is when selling the wine or deal with the complaint when the customer brings it back thinking the crystals are bits of glass. With sparkling wine the added complication is dealing with tartrate crystals at disgorging. They will act as a nucleation point for foaming and cause you to lose far more wine than you can afford.

So, how to prevent this happening? There are a few options and most of them are expensive. First of all, barrel-fermented and aged wines are often naturally cold stable. A combination of being aged on the lees, a greater surface to volume ratio for precipitation in the barrel and a smaller vessel getting colder during the winter all contribute to the stability. But do not assume this – get the wine tested before you bottle it.

Physical cold-stabilisation by chilling the wine below zero, ideally to -4°C, and holding it there for several weeks can also perform the process naturally. This is impractical for most wineries and is not advised. Doing the same but adding cream of tartar to act as a seed for the precipitation of tartaric acid is a better solution. There is some debate among winemakers about how long you need to keep the wine chilled and in contact with the cream of tartar, and it ranges from a few hours to 48 hours. In theory once the wine hits saturation point it will be stable and any further chilling time will not do anything more. It is only trial and error that will tell how your wines will behave.

It is vital that you cold-stabilise your wine as the final process before filtration and bottling. Any other processes or additions such as blending or sweetening can render a stable wine unstable. The wine needs to be moving as it is chilled to prevent the liquid from freezing. Our relatively low-alcohol wines in the UK obviously have a higher freezing point than most. You also need to protect it from oxidation because oxygen is more soluble at low temperatures, making the wine vulnerable at this stage.

Most wineries will have a dedicated cold-stabilisation tank that has extra chilling capacity. If you don't have three-phase power in your winery, this operation and these low temperatures could prove quite tricky to achieve. Wrapping the tank in bubble wrap or other insulating material can help. You can also use a free-standing heat exchange unit that can be hooked up to individual tanks – these circulate the wine while chilling, and require a centrifugal pump that will be able to keep the wine moving without freezing up. There is also some concern about how gentle this process is – biodynamic winemaking prohibits the use of centrifugal pumps because of the perceived sheering of the wine as it is circulated.

Other methods of cold-stabilisation are electrodialysis, metatartaric acid or carboxymethylcellulose. Electrodialysis is quick, irreversible and uses significantly less power than physical cold-stabilisation. However, it requires a specialist machine and, while these are widely available for contract hire in Europe and New World wine regions, there isn't a single one in operation in the UK, as far as we are aware.

Metatartaric acid is an additive that can be used at bottling or disgorging to provide temporary stability by inhibiting the precipitation of crystals. It is fine for wines designed to be drunk within a year or so. The effectiveness of the treatment is very much dependent on what temperature the wine will be stored. If kept in a cool cellar at 10°C then it could remain stable for 18 months, while at 25°C it may only be a few months.

CMC is a new product for wine, approved for use in the EU only in the last few years. It has, however, been around as a food additive for many years. Its action, like metatartaric acid, is an inhibitory one, but it is more stable. However CMC can react with certain types of wine, leaving them cloudy.

It is worth noting that the last three methods do not significantly reduce the final acidity of a wine, unlike the physical cold-stabilisation. In some wine regions this is desirable because natural acidity is low anyway, but in the UK we are often battling high acidity, and the removal of tartaric acid at this stage is a bonus in helping to achieve the right balance. There are also possible quality issues with the final three methods. Most high-quality wineries use cold-stabilisation as the first choice, despite its high cost in terms of power usage and time. Electrodialysis is only really cost-effective in very large-scale production wineries. The use of additives to inhibit crystal formation is often considered a last resort for small batch winemaking and to rectify problems once in bottle (at disgorging for example).

Filtration

Most wines will need to be filtered prior to bottling, unless you are making a natural wine. For still wines it is necessary to ensure they are sterile-filtered to a 0.25 or 0.45 micron level. The numbers refer to the pore size of the filter, and indicate the type of foreign body the filter will remove. For example 0.25 will remove bacteria while 0.45 will remove yeast cells. If you make still wine in a winery where sparkling wine is also made and you retain some residual sugar in the wine, you will need to sterile filter to avoid unwanted secondary fermentation. It is also an aesthetic issue. Most consumers expect their wines to be bright and clear with no haze.

At bottling, white wines should have a turbidity measurement of no more than 1.5 NTU when measured on a nephelometer. Red wines can be higher but probably no more than 4 or 5 NTU at the most. To achieve this level of clarity you can choose from several types of filter:

Cross-flow filtration
These machines are very efficient but at €50,000 too expensive for all but the biggest wineries.

Pad filtration
Very traditional and found all over the world, a pad and frame filter is very versatile and relatively simple to use. The downside is the risk of a papery taste from the pads, unless they are flushed through with plenty of water first. There is also the risk that the wine will be watered down by this process, especially with small volumes. The pads themselves are cheap but are single use only, so unless you can filter several wines in one go, you need to have plenty of spares. They come in various sizes and you can buy pads to cope with different levels of filtration. A great advantage is that the first pads can be coarse filtration followed by finer filtration in the same movement, saving time and reducing the number of times the wines have to be moved.

Cartridge filtration
These come in many guises and sizes, and are simple to set up and use. A stainless steel housing contains removable cartridges so that you can use the same housing for varying levels of filtration. The cartridges themselves can be cleaned and stored for re-use in the same season, although it is not recommended to attempt to keep a cartridge for more than one vintage. They are more expensive to buy than the pads, but ease of use and ease of cleaning can out-weigh the cost.

Diatomaceous earth filtration
This is the classic method of filtration for sparkling wines including Champagne. However, DE filtration is rapidly falling out of favour. The

earth, a fine powder made up of the microscopic skeletons of long-dead sea creatures (diatoms) is found in the largest quantities in Germany (where it is known as kieselguhr) and Nevada and Colorado in the USA.

The earth offers inert filtration, neither imparting nor stripping out flavour. The drawbacks are the potential health risk to operators – breathing in the fine dust, although no longer thought to be carcinogenic, can damage the operative's lungs and cause skin conditions. A further disadvantage is the filtration machinery. It is made up of lots of moving parts, and a skilled operative is required to get the earth to coat the discs properly and form a good filtration aid. The final disadvantage is disposal of the earth once you have finished with it. It cannot be put down the drains and should not be thrown in the regular rubbish – there is a requirement to have it disposed of properly, which inevitably involves cost.

Lenticular filtration

This is a relatively recent innovation and one that is rapidly replacing DE filtration in Champagne and other quality sparkling wine regions, because it does a very similar job but without the health hazards and disposal problems. The great advantages are no moving parts to the filter; you just need a centrifugal pump (ideally, although a basic impeller will do the job) hooked up between the tank and filter. The filtration medium is a cellulose and is housed within discs negating the need for the operator to handle it. You do need to flush with water to remove any residual taste. The discs can be stored within the filter after use, with SO2 and citric acid to maintain them until the next use. Depending on the size of the winery you could expect to filter an entire vintage through the same discs.

Chapter Six

Bottling and labelling

The most crucial stage for any winemaker, this is where you can mess up an entire year's worth of wine if you don't get it right. Cleanliness and oxygen are the two most important factors for all types of wine, but most particularly still wines. As soon as a wine is bottled it starts on its path to becoming vinegar. Any bacteria introduced at bottling along with excess oxygen will speed up this process.

A lot of the sparkling wineries in the UK use the mobile bottling lines of the Institut Oenologique de Champagne (IOC). This takes out the need for a dedicated area within the winery. Also, as sparkling wines are going to be destined for a few years lees-ageing they can all be done in one go. The fast lines (up to 5,500 bottles per hour) are more efficient than most UK wineries could ever hope to justify owning, so the bottling is done in a few days. There is enough equipment in a winery that is only used for a few weeks of the year, there is no need to add a bottling line to this list.

Still wine bottling will have to be done on-site or shipped out in bulk and bottled under contract in another winery who does this (such as Bolney Wine Estate in West Sussex), or a specialist contractor as used by supermarkets and bulk shippers. However, the volumes required to make this viable are considerable and beyond the majority of UK wineries.

Manual bottling is a necessary evil for most small-scale wineries in the UK. Automatic bottling lines are expensive and require a certain volume to work efficiently. However, manual bottling carries a high risk of oxygen uptake. If you can flush the bottles with inert gas such as nitrogen or argon before filling you will have an advantage. Do not use carbon dioxide at this stage – the CO_2 will dissolve into the liquid and you will end up with an unintended spritz to the finished wine. Measuring the dissolved CO_2 of your wine is recommended, and you can adjust according to style; white wines should be in the region of 1,200-1,500 mg/l DCO_2 at bottling – if it is excessive you can sparge the wine in the tank with nitrogen to remove the CO_2. Red wines are usually bottled between 600-800mg/l.

Similarly you can measure the dissolved oxygen (DO_2) in the tank before bottling. It should be below 1-1.5mg/l – sparge with nitrogen to remove any excess. It is also advisable to then check the DO_2 again in the bottles – if the pick-up of oxygen is greater than 1mg/l you have a problem on the line and need to stop, tighten all the fittings, use nitrogen gas to sparge the bottles, etc.

Checking the fill-height as you proceed with bottling is also necessary, and legally you are obliged to do so and record your measurements. There are many types of still wine bottle and the standard 750ml size, whatever shape, will have a figure on the bottom indicating how many millimetres from the top the wine level should be at. It is usually somewhere between 63 and 73mm – measure with a ruler to ensure that Trading Standards will be happy with the consistency of your filling. It is better to be slightly over than under, but you can be penalised either way.

Cleaning your bottling line

Everything must be squeaky clean prior to bottling, and steam is the easiest and most efficient way to do this. You can use a combination of hot water, caustic soda and citric acid if steam is not available, but you need to be very thorough. Steam is absolutely vital if you are bottling still and sparkling wines on the same line. Yeast cells introduced into the sparkling bottles can hibernate and survive from one season to the next. Steam is the only reliable cleaning method that will get into all the nooks and crannies of a bottling line.

If you are lucky enough to be able to justify and afford an automatic bottling line you need to consider the following before purchase:

- **Speed**: How many bottles per hour? Can you keep up? Will it do your small volumes as well?
- **Closures**: Can you choose screw-cap, cork, crown cap and interchange between all three?
- **Inert gas**: Can you flush the bottles with gas automatically?
- **Bottle type**: Can you use burgundy, Bordeaux and sparkling bottles? Half-bottles, magnums? How adjustable is the line?

- **Labels**: Will it fit the type of labels you want? It is easier and cheaper to fit labels to the line rather than vice versa, but you need to make sure the line is compatible, especially if you have an odd-shaped design.
- **Labour**: How many people are required to operate the line efficiently? Would it be worth spending money on conveyors and turntables in the line to reduce the number of people required?

Analysis

Trying to make wine without any kind of analysis is like trying to drive blindfolded. You can do it and you might be all right for a while, but an accident is inevitable sooner or later. Some of the basic analysis kits can be bought quite cheaply, and being able to check certain parameters on site can speed up decision-making at all stages. There are sevearl laboratories in the UK offering dedicated analysis for wine producers.

The cost of testing a sample for a 500-litre batch of wine is the same as it is for a 5,000-litre batch, so the smaller you are the higher the cost; but knowledge is power, and if you can pre-empt a problem, prevent oxidation, fine-tune your filtration, avoid unnecessary stabilisation processes and monitor volatile acidity, you will save money every time. Testing a wine for cold-stability might cost £15 or more, but if you discover that one wine out of 20 doesn't require cold-stabilisation, you will have saved the outlay in power alone. Likewise, re-bottling a wine that has proved unstable once bottled will cost you much more than any analysis would have done in the first place.

The parameters tested for the PDO and PGI Wine Schemes are as follows:

Still wines

1. Actual and total alcoholic strengths: a minimum of 8.5 per cent; actual alcoholic strength. Total alcoholic strength must not exceed 15 per cent.

2. Reducing sugars: no parameters set: for information only.

3. pH – no parameters set: for information only.

4. Total acidity: a minimum of 4g pr litre expressed as tartaric acid.

5. Volatile acidity: a maximum of: 1.08mg per litre in white and rosé wines; 1.2mg per litre in red wine

6. Total sulfur dioxide: the maximum total sulfur dioxide is:

For wines with sugar levels below 5g per litre:

150mg per litre for red wine;

200mg per litre for white and rosé wines.

For wines with sugar levels above 5g per litre:

200mg per litre for red wines;

250mg per litre for white and rosé wines.

For wines with sugar levels above 45g per litre:

300mg per litre.

7. Free sulfur dioxide: a maximum of 45mg per litre for dry wines as defined in Part B, Annex XIV of Regulation 607/2009; a maximum of 60mg per litre for other wines.

8. Copper: a maximum of 0.5mg per litre.

9. Iron: a maximum of 8mg per litre.

10. Sterility: there must be no indication of yeast or bacteria liable to cause spoilage of the wine.

11. (a) Protein stability: the wine must remain unchanged in appearance after being held at 70°C for 15 minutes and subsequently cooled to 20°C.

11. (b) No-fault tasting: the no-fault tasting (and appeals) can be carried out by the WineGB Wine Scheme Manager; he will ensure that the wine is deemed commercially acceptable.

Sparkling wines

The parameters for PGI and PDO sparkling wines are very similar to the above, with the addition of a pressure test on the bottle showing at least 3.5 bar pressure plus cold-stability with the wine being clear of tartrate crystals after 36 hours at 2°C. Total SO_2 is also set at 185mg/l for sparkling wines. There are some extra parameters for the top-level PDO scheme, but they are essentially very similar.

Campden BRI is the laboratory in the UK that runs these schemes **www.campdenbri.co.uk** and all the details for applying can be obtained from the WineGB website or from Campden BRI direct.

If you need to check that your wines are within the required parameters before sending off your application for PGI/PDO you can send them into Campden BRI for a Corkwise Certificate of Analysis separately or to the another laboratory in the UK.

You should familiarise yourself with these tests and why they are carried out, as an understanding of that will help with your quality control in the winery.

Storage, riddling and disgorging

If you are making sparkling wine in the traditional, bottle-fermented method you need plenty of storage for the lees-ageing period. You could have five years' production in storage at a time. To cut down on space required you can layer the bottles by hand in free-standing stacks. Stillage cages that are forkliftable are more convenient and save time but do need more room.

The storage should be within your bonded warehouse area, it should be completely dark with no natural light and preferably low-UV light bulbs and temperature-controlled between 12-16°C.

Your riddling equipment should also be in a dark room where natural light cannot affect the wine – particularly rosés in clear glass bottles. The machines for this process require space, access and three-phase power. The yeast that was introduced at bottling has done its job of creating the bubbles through the second fermentation and providing flavour during the ageing process – autolysis – as the dead yeast cells break down. To remove the yeast and leave a clean, bright wine the riddling process gradually twists and adjusts the bottles until they are completely inverted.

You will also need room for disgorging equipment, corking machines and wire hood applicators. How automated this is will depend on the size of your production. For an average-sized UK sparkling winery you will need a semi-automatic line to be able to physically keep up with your production.

After riddling, the bottles are then carefully transferred to have their necks submerged in a freezing glycol bath (at –26°C). Once the plug of yeast is frozen the bottles are rinsed, the crown cap is removed, the frozen plug of yeast is ejected and the bottle is topped up with a sugar and wine solution according to what level of dosage (sugar addition) is required. A cork is inserted and secured with a wire hood. The wine then needs to be returned to storage for some post-disgorging time to allow the dosage liqueur to meld into the wine before being ready to package and sell.

Oeno Concept in Epernay are the inventors of the Gyropalette, the automated riddling machines. The company also supplies the cages and disgorging equipment. There are other suppliers of such equipment but most UK wineries use Oeno Concept equipment **www.oenoconcept.fr**.

Packaging and dispatch

Do not underestimate the amount of room you will need for dry goods storage: crown caps, bidules, corks, capsules, foils, glass bottles, cardboard boxes, chemicals, yeasts and additives. All these need to be stored in dry conditions, so the main winery is not suitable. Cardboard packaging should be kept well away from moisture; it can be a source of Trichloroanisole (TCA) in a winery, especially when wet. Consider using plastic pallets rather than wooden ones; these can also harbour TCA bacteria and moulds.

Labelling and bottle-washing machines all need space to operate, as well as room for packing into boxes and loading on to pallets. Can the forklift access the area to load the pallets on to trucks? Even if you are small enough scale to be doing this all by hand, you still need space in which to do it.

This area must also be extra secure – packaged wines are a lot easier to steal than single bottles in storage, or indeed wines in a tank or barrel. At this stage you have also declared how many bottles you have produced and HMRC will be expecting duty to be paid on each and

123

every bottle as soon as it leaves the bonded area. You need to make sure that your liability for duty is protected (both as a requirement under bonded warehouse regulations and to protect your own revenue).

Think about using six-bottle or 12-bottle boxes. In weight, 12 bottles of sparkling wine are incredibly heavy and the box itself would have to be fairly substantial. In total 12 bottles of still wine weigh approximately 17kg, which is fine for one person to lift.

Labelling

Details of labelling regulations including mock-ups are carried on the WineGB website **www.winegb.co.uk** and are updated as they change, which is virtually all the time. The Food Standards Agency is responsible for policing labelling regulations and wine production and can also offer advice on the subject.

The old Quality Wine Schemes have been replaced with Quality Wine becoming Protected Designation of Origin (PDO), Regional Wine becoming Protected Geographic Indication (PGI) and Varietal Wine as a new category. Table Wine is officially known as wine without geographic indication. The disputes and appeals currently ongoing are regarding the use of 'English' or 'Welsh' wine as a descriptor on the label – as it stands only PDO and PGI wines can use these terms in certain contexts. This comes under the 'Traditional Expression' section detailed below. There are also tighter restrictions on the grape varieties permitted and winemaking practices allowed for the PDO and PGI categories.

The basics that are unlikely to change are taken from the Food Standards Agency guidelines, according to Quality Categories:

For table wine, or wine without a geographic designation the following compulsory details must be visible on a label without having to turn the bottle:
- Wine/Country of origin
- Bottler's details

- Nominal volume
- Actual alcoholic strength

The following compulsory details are not required in the same field of vision:
- Lot number
- Contains sulphites (or Contains sulphites, sulfur dioxide), in English and other listed allergens

Optional items
Limited optional items are permitted for non-geographic wine e.g. brand name, colour, residual sugar description (e.g. dry, medium dry, see page 128). Further details are permitted if they do not conflict with specified information and they do not mislead to a material degree. More details below.

Varietal wine category
Only wine approved under a Varietal Wine Certification Scheme can show vine variety(ies) and/or vintage.

For Protected Geographical Indication (PGI) and Protected Designation of Origin (PDO) categories

The following compulsory details must be visible on a label without having to turn the bottle:
- Country of origin
- A geographical designation
- A traditional expression
- Protected Geographical Indication/ Protected Designation of Origin
- Bottler details – name, local administrative address and member state of the responsible bottler; plus exact place where the actual bottling took place if different. Preceded by the words – 'Bottled by' or 'Bottler'

- Nominal volume.
- Actual alcoholic strength.

The following compulsory details are not required in the same field of vision:

- Lot number
- Contains sulphites (or Contains sulphites, sulfur dioxide), in English

PDO and PGI optional items – still wine

Specified optional items permitted include trademarks (brand name), traditional terms, colour, vine variety, vintage. Further details are permitted, providing they do not mislead to a material degree:

- Vine variety – one variety: minimum 85 per cent from the named variety; 2+ varieties: 100 per cent of varieties, in descending order.
- Vintage – wine must be from at least 85 per cent of the named vintage.
- Trademark – trademarks may not be used if they conflict with protected traditional terms or more generally contain misleading information.
- Residual sugar level – for still wines, terms including dry, medium dry, medium, medium sweet, sweet are defined in Regulation 607/2009 – see Annex XIV.
- Traditional terms – 'methods of production'. Specified terms which have been notified by member states and third countries listed in Annex XII.B of Regulation 607/2009 may only be used by those countries for the category(ies) of wine specified. Examples include 'Château' (France, Luxembourg), 'Reserva' (Spain, Chile).
- Vineyard terms – Specified descriptions may be used only by countries which have notified these to the EC and are listed in Regulation 607/2009 Annex XIII.
- Community symbol – Protected Geographical Indication or Protected Designation of Origin – The symbol authorised by

Case study
Control in the winery – Stopham Vineyard, West Sussex
www.stophamvineyard.co.uk

In his first year Simon Woodhead had frost, and one year in June heavy rain knocked the flowers off the vines, more than halving yields. But Simon, who founded Stopham Vineyard at Pulborough, West Sussex, in 2007, wasn't put off.

"Weather is the key challenge to yield in England," he says. "It's said that for every three years there is one bad year, one medium year and one good year."

But Simon believes that whatever headaches the British weather brings with it, production will still be viable as long as the winemaking itself is rigorously controlled to produce absolute top quality. For while yields are important, quality brings demand; and with demand comes the opportunity for premium pricing. And he firmly believes that the only way to achieve a consistently top-quality wine is to obsess about detail – which, as a one-time engineering designer for the TAG McLaren Formula 1 team, he's well used to doing.

Two critical pieces of kit at Stopham are the thermometer and a CO_2 sensor. Simon aims for fermentations to last from four to six weeks to preserve the delicate aromatic characteristics of English wine. The CO_2 sensor measures the rate of fermentation and activates the temperature regulation equipment on each fermentation tank. Crucial blending and fining trials are conducted in a well-equipped laboratory to remove any traces of bitterness and astringency from the wine. Finally, an inert gas sterile bottler ('monoblock') is vital to protect the aromas. This helps prevent oxidation and bacteria in the wine.

Sustainability is very important and because they have sandy loam soil this free-draining soil minimises the run-off to the rivers Arun and Rother. They do not plough the site regularly which allows the grass to cover the entire vineyard which reduces the run-off and erosion.

Looking after the soil improves the quality of the grapes and they add manure from the cattle on the estate to improve the soil structure.

the EC may only be used in addition to the wine category descriptions or Traditional Expression (for authorised colour versions see Regulation 628/2008).

- Get the PDO/PGI symbols from the WineGB website.

Residual sugar labelling indicators (still wine)

- **Dry**   Maximum of 4 g/L, or 9 g/L where the total acidity content is not more than 2 g/L below the residual sugar content.
- **Medium Dry**   The residual sugar content must exceed the maximum for 'Dry' but not exceed 12g/l, or 18g/l where the total acidity content is not more than 10 g/Lbelow the sugar content.
- **Medium or Medium Sweet**   The residual sugar content must exceed the maximum for 'Medium Dry' but not exceed 45 g/L.
- **Sweet**   At least 45 g/L.

PDO and PGI – Sparkling wine, compulsory particulars

The following information must appear on a label in one field of vision:

- Wine/Country (provenance)
- Category of product, one of the following defined terms: Sparkling /Quality sparkling wine /Aerated sparkling wine
- Indication of sugar content
- Nominal volume
- Actual alcoholic strength
- The producer or a vendor

The following compulsory details are not required in the same field of vision:

- Contains sulphites (or Contains sulphites, sulfur dioxide), in English

PDO and PGI optional items – sparkling wine

- Allowed for i) sparkling wine with protected designation of origin or geographical indication; ii) sparkling wine and aerated sparkling wine recognised as varietal;
- Vine variety – one variety: minimum 85 per cent from the named variety;
  2+ varieties: 100 per cent of varieties, in descending order;
- Vintage – minimum 85 per cent of stated year;
- Allowed for sparkling wine with protected designation of origin or geographical indication;
- Protected designation of origin/protected geographical indication.

EC wines: one of these terms must be shown together with a geographical indication, unless a traditional term listed by the EC is shown – see eBacchus **http://ec.europa.eu/agriculture/markets/wine/e-bacchus/**

- Community symbol - protected designation of origin/ protected geographical indication;
  The symbol authorised by the EC may only be used in addition to the wine category descriptions.

The current debate for sparkling wines of PDO quality is which grape varieties are allowed to be used. The most recent list is: Pinot Noir, Pinot Noir Précoce, Pinot Meunier, Chardonnay, Pinot Gris, Pinot Blanc. This has caused a few quality sparkling wine producers to feel marginalised for their use of varieties such as Auxerrois. As mentioned before, the whole situation with regards to PDO/PGI regulation is very fluid at the moment, so keep an ear open for new developments.

Chapter Seven
Marketing

Having no tradition of domestic production has made Britain one of the most sophisticated wine markets in the world. Without its own wines to prefer and protect, Britain has been open to imports from every wine-growing country on the planet. In the pre-Common Market days when wine duties were high, the middle classes and the better-off drank classic wines from France, Germany and Northern Italy and fortified wines from Spain, Portugal, Sicily and the Canaries. In the 1960s and 70s, licensing reform, the growth of package holidays and Common Market accession dramatically increased wine's availability, created mass awareness and demand, and finally made wine affordable to everybody. Britain became a target market for producers from Bulgaria, Romania, Australia, New Zealand, California, South Africa, Argentina, Chile… without the opening up of the British market, how many of these countries would even have wine industries of much note?

The size and sophistication of the British market – and the average British wine-drinker can probably name and identify more grape varieties than most French drinkers – ought to put English producers at an advantage, but actually it's not so easy. English wines have to compete with all comers. The UK consumer is used to well-made, fruity, high-alcohol, good-value wines that they can buy for £6 or less. Trying to explain that we, in English and Welsh vineyards, have to contend with low yields, poor weather, erratic harvests, high labour costs, etc. is not good marketing. It is negative, and the consumer might respond with sympathy, but you still haven't given them a positive reason to spend a little more on your wine. Our wines can also be well made, but we need to accentuate the differences in a positive fashion – subtlety, aromatic rather than fruity, lower in alcohol and still good value at £10+ for table wines, £25+ for sparkling.

It is not an impossible challenge; New Zealand wine producers make far more wine than their tiny domestic market could possibly consume. They are geographically a long way from anywhere else in the world yet rely heavily on exports. We in the UK have a domestic population that could, in theory, drink our production several hundred times over without shipping further than a couple of hours. And New Zealand wines are expensive – in fact they carry the highest average price per bottle in the UK, even taking into account the super expensive wines of the classic French regions. This has not stopped them being successful in the UK.

The marketing campaign of the New Zealand Winegrowers Association has tied in with the national tourism campaign of New Zealand generally: clean, green, 100 per cent pure New Zealand. Sustainability and carbon footprinting of wineries has been led by the NZ winegrowers. Consumers are prepared to pay a bit more for a product they perceive as premium quality (and it helps that the ubiquitous Marlborough Sauvignon Blanc is recognisable to even the most uneducated palate). The New Zealanders haven't got everything completely right and have faced problems arising from over-production, but their strategy as a cohesive group of winegrowers is certainly worth studying.

In the UK there is a central vineyard/producer organisation in the form of Wines of Great Britain Limited **www.winegb.co.uk** (WineGB for short), formed in 2017 from the merger of the two former industry bodies, UK Vineyards Association and English Wine Producers.

Any serious entrant to the UK industry should become a member of this organisation as and when they are eligible to do so. If you want to have a say in the future of the industry, it is worth joining. Ready advice and resources are available to members and a number of initiatives are in the pipeline to bring added support to growers and producers. This includes dialogue with government on a national to local level, ensuring the right representation for the industry with tourism, planning and export initiatives and that the industry is consulted in all legislative matters concerning viticulture and winemaking.

While you are in the planning stages it would be worth attending the industry's annual trade and press tasting held in London, usually in May. You can judge the competition and standard of winemaking you will be up against, plus see WineGB in action. The tasting attracts a serious number of wine trade buyers and wine journalists.

What is your marketing plan?

Marketing is a function that many people, especially those whose businesses might fall within the broad category of 'alternative' or 'artisanal', sometimes sneer about as if it were superficial and even bordering on the mendacious. Actually, it's a central part of your business, embracing the nature of your wine, the constraints of production capacity, the demographic you intend to present your wine to and the way you aim to present. For instance, your strategy will be very much dependent on the size of your production; there is no point approaching Tesco if you only have 10,000 bottles to sell. With over 2,000 stores in the UK, if you were to sell one bottle of your wine per week in each of their stores, you'd need at least 100,000 bottles a year to supply them alone. Now, obviously not every branch carries every line, but this is a crude illustration of the scale on which these supermarkets operate.

Even if you were planning on producing 100,000 bottles per year it would be unwise to totally rely on one client for 100 per cent of your sales. A change of buyer or commercial strategy could see your listing removed at a stroke with no place to go. This chapter is not intended to bash the supermarkets, in fact they can be very valuable outlets as a vineyard's production grows, but care should be taken with the marketing mix to ensure that they are not the sole or majority market for your wine.

A new vineyard will take at least three years to produce a crop, and another two or three before it comes into full production. At first, then, you'll only have a small supply for which you have to find a market. These early years, while the work in the winery will probably not keep you fully employed, are the time to test and refine your marketing strategy while keeping things fairly low key. The marketing and branding decisions you make now will have far-reaching consequences, so it's just as well to take every opportunity to find out what works and what doesn't, and make whatever adjustments are necessary.

One early pitfall can be avoided by bearing in mind that naming

Case study
Word of mouth — Breaky Bottom Vineyard, East Sussex
www.breakybottom.co.uk

Pioneering Peter Hall planted his first vines in 1974 in the stunningly beautiful Breaky Bottom, a hidden valley folded deep in the heart of the South Downs. The setting alone is worth the trip down the mile-long rutted farm-track that is the vineyard's only means of access, but the quality of the wines is every bit as breathtaking as the scenery, and few visitors leave without their car being weighed down with bottles.

Marketing might not be a function that Peter would actually recognise, but whether by default or design he has hit the target perfectly. It helps that supply is limited by the size of the property and by what Peter can accomplish mainly on his own, albeit with the help of a dedicated band of friends and family. Harvest each year sees a group of the willing, children included, volunteering to pick the crop in return for lunch and the sheer enjoyment of the experience. It doesn't necessarily make for the most efficient picking, but it does make for a high local profile.

A regional listing with Waitrose not only accounts for significant volume but reinforces the local pride felt by consumers. It also makes Breaky Bottom wine a low food-miles product that is delivered direct to the stores themselves, cutting out the usual journeys to and from a central depot. Sustainability is increasingly important as a marketing tool, and this concentration on the markets that are both local and sustainable creates a loyal following of customers in the district who love to visit the vineyard themselves.

Quality, though, is vital to retaining their loyalty, and perhaps perversely Breaky Bottom had stuck doggedly with Seyval Blanc, proving year after year that it's a variety that can produce world-class sparkling wine with a unique English twist. As a hybrid, Seyval Blanc is not ranked among the top-quality English wine grapes, but Peter has shown repeatedly that with the right care in the vineyard and attention in the winery, it can compete with the best of the Champagne varieties. Breaky Bottom sparkling wines have been in Hugh Johnson's Top 10 for more than 20 years; in the 2013 International Wine & Spirit Competition it was rated Britain's Best Wine Producer; it's stocked in the government's cellars at Lancaster House and is wheeled out at official shindigs such as those attending the 2012 Olympics and the Queen's 60th Jubilee. On a less elevated plane, Breaky Bottom was also a stop for James May and Oz Clarke on their TV series *Drink to Britain.*

Today Seyval Blanc is still the principal variety but now Peter grows Chardonnay, Pinot Noir and Pinot Meunier. He makes two cuvées each year and ages them in bottle for at least four years. At release, he dedicates every wine to the memory of a close friend or relative. Five wines are currently available.

Natural England supports Breaky Bottom through the Higher Level Stewardship Scheme 'to conserve wildlife, maintain and enhance landscape quality and character and protect the natural environment.'

Their holding is made up of a six acre vineyard surrounded by steep hillsides grazed by sheep. The traditional flint barn and farmhouse, originally built in 1827, form the boundaries of what was once a winter cattle yard.

The vineyard has improved its quality control yet further by installing temperature-controlled fermenters and cellarage; and it's this insistence on high quality, low volume, and a close connection with its customers rather than high-profile marketing that has generated word-of-mouth recommendation stretching all the way from Waitrose stores in East Sussex to the highest echelons of government.

your product after your vineyard might be a seriously limiting factor a bit further down the road. The law says that if a wine is named after a specific vineyard then all the grapes in the wine must come from that vineyard; so if you've taken that step but then find you have to expand and either buy in extra fruit or plant new vineyards, you will almost certainly have to rebrand completely – an expensive, risky and time-consuming exercise. You might have noticed that some of the best-known names in English wine – Nyetimber, Ridgeview, Chapel Down, Camel Valley – don't refer to any vineyard on their labels; all of them source grapes from outside their original estate vineyards so cannot use that term. It doesn't appear to have done them any harm!

But marketing isn't only about selling as much as humanly possible. Life is simpler for vignerons who put the focus entirely on quality rather than quantity and know they can sell all they make and run a viable business without ever having to expand. For them, the art lies in managing demand. Being hard to get hold of, either through limited production and high demand, or selectively releasing stock and selling on an allocation basis, can create a buzz around a wine. Nothing makes a luxury product (and English wine, particularly sparkling wine, is in the luxury bracket) more appealing than the impression of unavailability.

Waiting lists, allocated stock, tiered buying (where the customer has to purchase one case of the lower-end wines to qualify to purchase six bottles of the top release) are all strategies adopted throughout the winemaking world. In California, top-end Napa Valley wineries have in the past very effectively managed their customers and stock to maintain their high prices. Screaming Eagle in Oakville (**www. screamingeagle.com**) is a case in point; its website allows customers to join the waiting list, with the disclaimer that this does not give you the right to buy their wine, only that you may be moved onto the 'active list' as spaces become available. In Burgundy, the smaller, more in-demand domaines will allocate stock to merchants based on their buying history, allowing each client to buy a limited number of the grand crus on condition that they also buy a stated volume of the premiers crus and village wines. Domaine de la Romanée Conti is a classic example.

As far as it is possible to tell, these practices have not been either tried or necessary in the UK, but as demand increases for the top sparkling wines, and supply takes its time to catch up, this might become a part of the English wine industry.

Reaching your potential customers – starting small

Your neighbours, friends and family are a good place to start. Get local people involved with the vineyard at planting by sponsoring a vine, hosting a village party amongst the vines or, later on, getting them to help with the picking at harvest time. It will engage them and get them on your side, and they will be ambassadors for your product wherever they go. It is a small start, but you never know whose radar you might appear on because of it.

However, this strategy will only take you so far and you will have to invest more time and money into marketing and branding your product as production grows. Your next stage will be to approach local independent wine merchants and other upmarket retailers who have the autonomy to list what they want. Localism is big in independent retail. Be prepared to give your time and samples to support them in consumer events and tastings at the start and throughout your relationship. One advantage of dealing with local retailers is delivery costs are lower – you can do them yourself.

Local restaurants and gastropubs should also be obvious outlets for your products. English wine is often described as needing to be 'hand-sold', meaning that every bottle has to be recommended by an ambassador. You need to convert the owners of local restaurants, their sommeliers, wine waiters and bar staff to your product. Hold tastings in-house for the staff to find out for themselves how good your wine is. Invite them to the winery for a tour and tasting, visit the vineyard with them and explain the philosophy behind your winemaking. People love a story and a personal connection. Give them a reason to champion your wine and they will do the hard work for you.

Wineclubs

There are a number of large wine clubs operating in the UK and some of the big ones are:

The Wine Society **www.thewinesociety.com**
Naked Wines **www.nakedwines.com**
Stone, Vine & Sun **www.stonevine.co.uk**
Virgin Wines **www.virginwines.co.uk**
Berry Bros and Rudd **www.bbr.com**
Monopole **www.connaughtwinecellars.com**
The Daily Drinker **www.thedailydrinker.co.uk**

Tapping into tourism

If you're on a tourist trail or located in a tourist destination, you're lucky in that other people will have done the hard work of getting the consumers to your doorstep for you; all you have to do is get them to buy some wine. And don't underestimate how much money people will spend when they're on holiday and feeling good about life. Consumers who would normally spend £6 a bottle in the supermarket and think they were splashing out might easily spend twice that on a bottle bought from the vineyard after a friendly tour and tasting.

Producers in the West Country have a fresh batch of holidaymakers from all over the UK and abroad every summer, but may struggle in the off-season when the weather puts off all but the hardiest of ramblers. A vineyard in the stockbroker belt of Hampshire won't see nearly as many tourists as its neighbours in the New Forest. When you set up your cellar door sales, think about how much traffic you can reasonably expect, and will it be passing trade? Can you entice people in by leaving leaflets at local B&Bs, pubs and hotels, as well as the tourist office? Be mindful, too, of what restrictions the local planning and licensing authorities might have imposed before going too far down this route. You will need to make sure you are legally allowed to receive visitors and sell your wine direct.

It is worth talking to the local tourist office to gauge your tourist potential. Identify the staff and managers/owners of other local tourist spots who might send people on to you. Invite them to the winery for a tasting and get them to sell your winery as a tourist destination. This can work particularly well with local pubs that stock your wine.

If you have any other talents or hobbies, such as music or sport, could you host an event or concert that might attract a wider audience to your vineyard? You can then sell your wine to the audience or participants, along with other refreshments. If your vineyard is part of a larger farm, you could run a harvest festival (the main arable crops are conveniently harvested before the grapes). If you have livestock, is it possible to offer a 'petting zoo' to attract families? While the children are occupied with lambs or goats, the parents can be tempted with a tasting and hopefully a purchase to take home.

See Chapter 8 for more on tours and tourism.

Farmers' markets

Farmers' markets are another outlet that can prove useful testing grounds for your wines. They require significant time at weekends and during the week, and you need to be a regular attender to attract a loyal following. Factor in this time commitment to your business plan, and don't forget to cost your time as well as the direct costs of the stall. Choose your venues carefully, and visit as a customer to see what the competition is in terms of other vineyards. Try to gauge the customer base and the popularity. Be prepared to lose money on the rainy days and average your takings over the season.

The great advantage of a market stall is the chance to meet your customers face-to-face – if you're offering samples (probably obligatory at these events) you get instant feedback. Use this information – you can attempt to formalise it by asking customers who taste the wine to make a brief comment on a card, including their contact details to add to your customer database. Alternatively, run a business card draw offering a bottle of wine as the prize to encourage people to give you their contact details. The Gambling Act 2005 covers prize draws and there are rules that can be found online at the Gambling Commission website **www.gamblingcommission.gov.uk**, but as long as the draw is open to anyone (over 18, particularly when alcohol is the prize) and free to enter, you will not fall foul of the law.

Case study
High-profile public relations —
Camel Valley Vineyard, Cornwall
www.camelvalley.com

Cornwall's Camel Valley Vineyard scored a tremendous public relations coup in 2012 when it applied for Protected Designation of Origin for a 1.5ha area of its estate. It was a move that grabbed headlines as a national first, because as things stood at the time there were only two PDOs in the entire UK – England and Wales.

Camel Valley's application related to the planted parts of a tiny but geologically distinct area of the estate known as Darnibole after the adjoining (and world-renowned) Delabole slate quarries. The area covered by the PDO was quite distinctive with slate subsoil, optimum slope-to-height ratio and a long, cool growing season with ideal rainfall; absolutely perfect for the Bacchus grapes with which they were planted, the vineyard's owner Bob Lindo argued.

The story was covered by the BBC, local and national news, *Decanter*, *The Drinks Business*, *Harpers* and numerous wine blogs and more general food and tourism websites; so for a relatively small investment in time, and not much money either, Camel Valley had generated a huge amount of attention.

Somewhat later and after five years of scrutiny by the 28 Member States, the EU unanimously agreed on elevating the PDO to the highest level at a meeting held on 25 April 2017. They had been so impressed by the application that the area was extended during the process, from 7 acres to 28 acres of south-facing land in the Camel Valley, all part of Camel Valley's vineyards.

But the Lindo family's PR expertise is not restricted to Darnibole Bacchus, it extends to Camel Valley's entire range of wines. The strategy is simple: enter every competition going and if the wine's up to scratch its success will create a huge reputation and generate vast publicity. Sam, Bob's son, is the winemaker at Camel Valley, and between 2006–2011 was WineGB Winemaker of the Year three times and runner-up twice.

Darnibole Bacchus has won numerous gold medals over the years, but it's not alone – the entire range is successful. Here's the medal tally for the last few years. 2015: three golds; 17 silvers; 20 bronzes, two commendations; 2014: 19 medals all told; 2013: 13; 2012: 42. Sam and Bob's watchwords are: "make good wine, win something, tell people" and: "consistency at every level – no excuses".

Quality winemaking is at the heart of their business, as it should be, and the wines do their own marketing. Camel Valley is a prime example of how awards and competitions can be a crucial part of a marketing and publicity campaign if handled correctly. It costs money to enter competitions and also requires investment in terms of time, and if you win an award you really need to turn up to accept it to gain maximum exposure.

With that in mind another sucess was when in 2017 their 2013 Camel Valley brut sparkling wine was chosen by British Airways to be served in their First Class cabin. The order, the biggest in the history of Camel Valley, followed a blind tasting of Champagnes and sparkling wines overseen by Andy Sparrow, head of wine retail at Bibendum wine distributors. Said Andy: "Camel Valley got this on merit and scored really highly in the tasting. Well done to them."

Remember that unlike most stallholders at a farmers' market, you are selling alcohol, and will need a personal licence to do so (see page 160 for more on licensing). This also means that whoever holds that licence will need to be present on the stall, or at least within shouting distance.

Most farmers' markets are run by local councils or on local council property, such as the high street of a market town. You will also need to apply to the local council of each venue where you intend to sell for a Temporary Event Notice (TEN). Because most farmers' markets are held outdoors, it is not practical for the organisers to have a premises licence, making the TEN a necessity. It shouldn't be a problem because in most cases the issuing authority will also be the market organiser; however, there is a fee of £21 for a TEN each time you set up your stall. This is in addition to the stall fee you will be charged. These fees vary from market to market, and don't forget to check whether you get a stand, canopy, table, etc. included with your fee.

Finding your local farmers' markets is fairly straightforward. If the organisers of your nearest one are doing a half-decent job then you should have seen advertising in your local area. Try the local councils in a 30-mile radius of your vineyard, or a simple Google search will throw up some starting points. Also look at the National Farmers' Retail & Market Association **www.farma.org.uk**, and specifically the markets section at **www.localfoodadvisor.com**.

Cellar door sales

You need to decide whether you want to sell your wines from the cellar door, and to what extent. Will you have a dedicated tasting room and shop, and charge for tours and employ the hard-sell to each and every visitor, or will it be more ad hoc and by appointment only for bespoke tours? This decision will be influenced by your location – if you are on a tourist trail with lots of passing trade then you may find that having set opening hours and a dedicated member of staff to undertake tours and sell the wine will be worth the investment. Be aware that you will need a premises licence as well as a personal licence to sell alcohol off the premises. The local council's planning office will also take an interest: if you are selling only your own products, grown and made on site, then you will probably have no problem running tours and tastings by appointment; opening a shop with potential to sell other local produce and encouraging drop-in visitors is a different matter altogether, though. You're going to need planning permission.

A planning application can be a long drawn-out episode full of frustration and fear, or it can be a straightforward rubber-stamping job. Which of the two it turns into depends on the relationship between the applicant and the planning officer. The applicant needs to understand the principles, although not the fine details, of planning law. The guiding principles are that the structure and location should be suited to the neighbourhood and that the neighbours should be put to as little trouble as possible. Access, traffic, off-road parking and signage are all going to be factors.

Do not view the planning officers as the enemy – their job is not to prevent you doing business but to make sure that your business does not have a detrimental effect on the people living around you. Work with them and be prepared to do some homework yourself. Vineyards are not yet that common, and most planning officers will not have had to deal with one. There is some confusion within planning departments across the country as to exactly what category a vineyard and winery falls into. For your marketing plan the council will definitely become involved if you add a shop with the signage necessary to entice a worthwhile number of customers.

Press and PR

You won't want to try a serious launch until you have enough stock to sell, but some 'soft' marketing in advance won't do you any harm. Encourage any trade and press contacts you have to visit and taste your wine. Send out an initial press release announcing your arrival and broad-brushing your intentions, and follow it up with more when anything is happening in the winery or vineyard that warrants a photo opportunity: tanks being delivered, pickers working in the vineyard, the first disgorging or bottling – anything that makes a good photograph and has a bit of a story to go with it. Even if you can't get key people from the press or trade to come to the site, keep letting them know what is going on at crucial stages just to keep their attention/interest.

It is important to not only focus on the big-name consumer journalists but also target the writers for the trade magazines such as *Harpers, The Drinks Business*, etc. If the trade become aware of a new winery as it becomes established they might be more prepared to consider stocking the wine once it is available.

Don't forget the local press – they may not be wine specialists, but sometimes the national newspapers will pick up a story from the regional news and disseminate it further. Vineyards and wineries can be picturesque, offering a good filming or photographic opportunity for local television, web and print media.

Competitions

Once your wine is available for sale in bottle, an important part of achieving a profile and recognition is to enter some competitions. You can start with the Regional Vineyard Associations, most of which will hold a small competition. The WineGB Wines of the Year Competition is the first step outside your locale. Your wine will be up against the best (and the worst!) from the UK and if you manage to establish your wine's quality against its peers, that's a launchpad from which to blast off into the international arena. The wines are judged to international standards by 12 top wine experts that regularly judge the biggest international competitions. In 2017 the awards received 293 entries from producers across England and Wales, with 20 gold, 36 silver and 127 bronze medals awarded to winning wines.

The International Wine and Spirit Competition has a category for best sparkling wine in the world (outside Champagne), which Nyetimber has won at least twice. Ridgeview has won gold medals at the *Decanter* World Wine Awards. Chapel Down and Denbies Wine Estate have both scooped golds at the International Wine Challenge. These competition wins put

English wine, particularly English sparkling wine, firmly on the map. But to compete at this level, you need to be well prepared. Patience is required – early harvests tend not to be of fantastic quality, so only release a wine with decent lees-age in the case of sparkling, and from a good vintage, to stand a chance. You don't want to do badly and risk alienating the wine trade at an early stage.

The competitions you enter should be chosen with recognition, image and validity in mind: which award? Who is judging it? And what other wines will you be up against?

In 2017, in the *Decanter* World Wine Awawrds, there was a surprise when England's Winbirri vineyard scooped a Platinum best in show for its Bacchus 2015. The first time an English still wine has won one of DWWA's highest honours. Made from a single grape variety, namely Bacchus, a grape relatively un-touched by most of the wine world but which has found a home in the fledgling English wine industry.

Websites and online presence

A website is, of course, essential; Facebook and Twitter are still the two other obvious portals that offer a cheap and easy way to reach many potential customers and their friends. But you start with a website, and make sure it's a good one. It's the first point of contact for the vast majority of your potential customers; it's your shop window; and to a lesser extent, it's your retail counter.

The crucial thing to remember when embarking on a social networking presence is to be up to date. That needn't mean tweeting six times a day or updating your Facebook page/blog every hour, but it does mean that you need to have fresh content on a regular basis. People will lose interest if they see the same piece of news every time they log on. The benefit of Twitter is that it doesn't have to be ground-breaking news each time – in 280 characters you can let people know that you are pruning in the snow/sun/rain, that you are bottling your first vintage, prepping the winery for harvest, taking delivery of new tanks, designing a new label – anything and everything that you do towards getting your wine to the market can be tweeted. It requires a certain dedication, but needn't be hugely time-consuming.

Your website should be informative, and can tell the visitor more about the story of you and your vineyard, with lots of photographs and snippets of information along with an online shop when you have stock to sell. You can use it to advertise tastings, events and new releases, and drive people to it via your social networking activity. Running a website need not be expensive, and the cost of design can range from a few hundred pounds to thousands, depending on functionality. A webshop will be more expensive to set up and maintain than a simple, informative site. The hosting of a website can also be very inexpensive – the cost of hosting a website and domain name can be as low as £100 per year.

Visit as many other vineyard websites as you can, particularly those that are offering a similar product to you. When selecting a web designer make a note of your favourite winery websites and ensure that the person you select has a sympathetic style – you should be able to see other websites they have designed to make sure they will understand your style and ethos.

While having an online shop may seem tempting, and a cheap way to reach customers, you need to have the ability to ship your wine to your clients. This may not seem like a problem, but finding couriers who will take liquids is one thing, then finding one who will take liquid in a glass bottle is another. Should you surmount these problems and find a courier who will take your wine for shipping, you have to contend with the inevitable breakages, thefts and losses along the way. If one bottle breaks in a case it often means that the others become unsaleable as the labels are damaged. You then need to get that case back and re-dispatch to the customer.

With a good courier this shouldn't happen too often, but it will happen occasionally so you need to have a plan to cope with it and be making enough margin to absorb the costs. Not forgetting that one of these costs will be extra packaging to give your wine the best chance of making it to the customer in one piece. At least with wine being a fairly high-value product it is easier to absorb this cost, but margins are usually slim at the best of times, so don't forget to factor it in. The best way to find a good courier is also the simplest: order a few products from the biggest online wines, beers and spirits retailers in the country. The couriers and packaging they use have been tried, tested and found to be satisfactory.

When selling online and sending your product direct to the consumer, you will need a premises licence as well as your personal licence. Obtaining it should be a formality because there is no impact on the locality in terms of visitors and drinking on-site, but again it is a consideration that shouldn't be forgotten.

If you don't want to maintain an online shop, then your site can instead drive customers to your distributors and retailers. It is best to assess your technological limitations and work with them. If you are not naturally inclined towards a high-maintenance online presence, then use your site simply to provide information about your wines. If you don't already make use of Twitter, Facebook, LinkedIn and use e-commerce yourself, then you are unlikely to make a success of these options without feeling it is a lot of hard work. Having said that, if you have anyone working with you or a member of the family to whom an online life is second nature, then get them to do it for you.

Don't overlook the chance to collect data on your customers and website visitors while they are browsing. Offer them the chance to follow you on Twitter, link them to your Facebook page where they can 'friend' you and gather contact information via an email newsletter that people can sign up to. Make sure you then do actually send a regular newsletter offering the chance to buy early-release wines, inform people of progress in the vineyard and winery and invite them to events, etc. Be aware that collecting data from people means you must comply with the Data Protection Act 1998, essentially to ensure that you don't share anyone's data with others without their permission and don't use it for any reason other than that stated when it was collected. The most common error is sending a group email to your entire list without using the BCC (blind copy) function. Also to be taken into account is General Data Protection Regulation (GDPR) which came into affect in 2018.

Labels and packaging

Once your wine is out of your hands and sitting on the shelf of a shop, it needs to speak for itself at first glance. Unless there is a tasting going on, or the staff have decided/been persuaded to hand-sell your wine, then your label needs to do everything you would normally do to sell your wine and more. Remember, it will be sat on the shelf next to an endless array of other wines.

Still and sparkling wines have very different expectations held of them in terms of packaging. A still wine can afford to be a bit different and have a quirky or trendy design. Something along those lines can often help sales on looks alone. Think of the arty or graphic images on some of the first Australian and other New World wines that made it to the UK in the 1980s and 1990s. Sparkling wine, however, is a different story. The customer expects something a bit special when they spend the extra money on a Champagne or top-end sparkling wine. If you look at the range of English sparkling wines on the shelf they are all traditional in style and are often similar to Champagne labels with the use of serif fonts and gold or silver embossing.

If you have a range of wines, you will need to allow for the differences to be reflected in the labels while maintaining a consistent identity. This can be especially difficult if you offer both still and sparkling wines. A good label designer should be able to work around the problem once given a comprehensive brief. You will need to have an idea in mind about what level you are pitching at, and what image you want your labels to portray; a designer can only work with the information you give them. If you request a rustic feel that reflects your farming roots, you can't then complain that the label is not upmarket enough!

Legal labelling requirements have become slightly more complicated than they used to be as you now have to include information on allergens – does your wine contain nuts? – alongside the percentage alcohol by volume and content in centilitres; the full and up-to-date regulations are available on **www.food.gov.uk/business-industry/winestandards/wine-labelling**. But do remember that what the law considers your 'front' label, containing all the legal information, can to all intents and purposes be your back label. The retailer will make the decision as to which way round to face the bottle – if the clean lines and modern design of your back label are more attractive than the legal front label, there is no law that states the front label has to face front on the shelf! The customer also expects to turn the bottle around and read about the wine. This is your chance to tell them what you think of it, write your own tasting note, tell them what food to eat with the wine, and let them know where they can get more information via your website. Use a QR code to drive traffic to your website – a 'Quick Response' code allows the owner of a smartphone with a barcode reader app to scan the label and be taken to your webpage. This is your opportunity to persuade them to go ahead and buy the wine or tell them where they can buy it (if they have come across it at a friend's house or a bar), visit your winery, tweet to their followers that they just drank this wonderful wine, etc. The opportunities are endless.

Chapter Eight

Tours and tourism

Vineyard tourism is extremely popular in wine regions around the world, especially (of course) France but also New Zealand, California, Canada, Rioja, Australia, South Africa and the Rhine. A vineyard – almost any vineyard – is undoubtedly a fascinating place to visit, and the hard-headed grower has to take advantage of the fact. Opening your gates to the public is a very important step in the process of educating them in the joys and appreciation of wine in general, and your wine in particular.

The strategy of bringing the people in doesn't have to be confined to a stroll around the vines followed by a tasting and a bit of shopping. Other onsite activities, even if they're not strictly wine-related, still raise the profile of the winery and its brands, as well as generating income in their own right. Denbies Wine Estate in Surrey, for example, offers services for use by the general public including conference and wedding facilities, a restaurant, art exhibition space and even a vineyard train. Chilford Hall in Cambridgeshire is another vineyard and winery sited in a grand country house that runs a shop, a rather good bistro, functions, as well as an outside catering business to add to its vineyard tours.

Not all vineyards come as well-equipped as Chilford Hall (although a surprising number do), but even the smaller vineyards are attractive places to visit for a picnic, accompanied perhaps by a chilled bottle of the site's own product. Frankly, monoculture of any sort is visually dull whether it's mile upon mile of unbroken cornfield, the eerily quiet shadows of the conifer plantation, or hillsides coated with nothing but rows of vines. Smaller parcels of vines set among woods and meadows, as are common in England, give the eye the variety it craves.

Most growers and winemakers welcome tourists. However a handful see tourists and tourism as a distraction from the core business of making and selling top-quality wines. Others would love to exploit the opportunity but don't have the space or the facilities. Others still are put off by the costs – and indeed, the initial outlay required to build and equip a visitors' centre, café and off-licence plus the ongoing overhead of staffing and managing it can be prohibitive when there's always the risk of visitor numbers failing to match up to expectations.

But there are many activities that can bring in paying customers and also turn them into unofficial ambassadors for the vineyard and winery without implying a speculative injection of cash. 'Special occasion' open days with vineyard tours and wine tastings are a good starting point, and can be organised as part of (and therefore, publicity-wise, ride on the coat-tails of) almost completely unrelated events. Most towns and villages have an Open Garden Day – the vineyard can join in, with the publicity bonus of contributing the day's admission fees to the event's charity. On a national level, English Wine Week is organised by WineGB in the first week of June every year. If you want to bring in outside wine educators, then the Association of Wine Educators (AWE) – **www.wineeducators.com** – has a full list of members available for delivering wine courses and tastings. And don't forget, if you hold a personal licence (which you should) but no premises licence, a Temporary Event Notice will allow you to sell your wine by the glass and in bottle to the day's visitors. Do remember, though, that even if you only open for one-off events and special occasions you need exactly the same facilities for visitors with disabilities visit www.tourismforall.org.uk to find out everything you need to know about disabled access and facilities) and for cars and/or coach access and parking as you would if you were open regularly.

Before you decide, though, on the style and scale of visitor hospitality (if any) best suited to your business, do your research. Visit a range of vineyards and wineries, see for yourself what they do to attract visitors and, once they've got them, how they part them from their money. Assess how much investment and management resource goes into it and how much revenue comes out. But do remember, if your venture into tours and tourism is such as to constitute a 'material change of use', you need planning permission.

Vineyard and winery tours

Tours of your premises and facilities provide visitors with a memorable experience that can also culminate in wine sales and recommendations to family and friends. They can be organised for set times each week, or by appointment with the winery via your website or over the telephone, although the telephone is generally better than the website for closing a sale. After all, your website may be able to say 'sorry, that date is fully booked' when a tour is selected, but it can't follow up in an appropriately chatty, helpful tone with, "I tell you what, we've got six spaces free the following Saturday afternoon if you're interested".

Standard tours generally charge around £10 a head, depending on the vineyard, content of the tour, tour length, how many are in the group and whether it is led by a guide. Eglantine Vineyard in Nottinghamshire offers two-hour group tours for ten or more people for just £7 a head, whereas Nutbourne Vineyard in West Sussex charges £15 a head for tours of the vineyard, the lake and the beautiful converted mill. Some offer different packages for different prices – Holmfirth Vineyard in Yorkshire, for example, offers vineyard tours lasting 1.5–2 hours for £7.50, with the option of 'sparkling afternoon tea' for two at £34.99 and an 'adopt a vine' Platinum Package, also for two, at £44.99. Many tours are guided by existing staff or specially employed part-time seasonal staff. But a more prestigious tour guide definitely adds value: at Court Garden Vineyard in Sussex, for instance, the weekly small-group vineyard tours are conducted by the proprietor, Howard Corney. The fact that the owner is leading the tour in person flatters the guests, adds to the sense of occasion and helps to justify the tour's price of £16 a head. The group assembles in the beautiful Sussex Barn where they are served tea and homemade cake before listening to a short talk about the history of vine growing in England. They then go on a short walk around the vineyard and discuss the work that is carried out throughout the year. The tour concludes with a tasting of Court Garden's sparkling wines.

Promoting the tours can be a problem for the smaller vineyard for which they are definitely a sideline. Tours can be advertised in the leaflets routinely distributed to local hotels, B&Bs, pubs, restaurants, shops and, of course (where they survive), local tourist offices. Gift vouchers for tours can be sold as presents for future use, which generates positive cash-flow. Vineyard tours can be advertised via websites with booking either online or by telephone. (Business Companion **www.businesscompanion.info** provides information about the rules and regulations that apply to the sale of goods and services over the internet, telephone, by text or by mail order).

With the widespread use of social media and mobile technology, their use by UK vineyards to publicise tours and activities although slow to begin with, is now beginning to grow. like vineyards and wineries around the world, there is also limited use of Facebook pages, groups or events to promote tours or activities in the UK. There is now multiple use of vineyard and winery videos on YouTube. There are free, cheap apps that can rapidly reach many people, and an active social network presence can increase vineyard, winery and brand awareness, thereby increasing visitors to your business and your income. Regular updates, photographs, events and vineyard news can be posted on social network sites or tweeted.

Local tourism initiatives

New vineyards sometimes join forces with others in the area to promote a combined trail and tours, often in conjunction with the local tourist board. Some vineyards already do this independently, as with Tourism South East **www.visitsoutheastengland.com** and Visit the Heart of England **www.visitheartofengland.com**. Tourism initiatives, such as local food and drink campaigns as part of destination marketing, result in an increased awareness of your vineyard and winery via promotions on local tourism sites and participation in their local attraction marketing campaigns.

Country houses

Chilford Hall is far from being the only grand country manor that wine helps to keep weatherproof. Among the many historic and beautiful country houses in the UK that have vineyards planted in the grounds, Stanlake Park at Twyford in Berkshire is a stand-out example. The original test vineyard of 500 vines, planted in 1979, was called Thames Valley Vineyard (later changed to Valley Vineyards). Since then it has grown to 10-ha planted with more than 20,000 vines. Many different trellising systems are used, including some unique to the estate such as the Stanlake Bow and the Stanlake Ballerina, which is a variant of the Smart-Dyson Ballerina, a mid-height Sylvoz system. A 17th-century brick-built barn houses the winery, and other picturesque outbuildings (of which there are many) house the shop, café and conference/functions suite (weddings a speciality!).

The 800 year-old Squerryes Court at Westerham, Kent, also has a vineyard among its many attractions, while Broadfield Court at Bodenham, Herefordshire, is a medieval manor house where 50 experimental vines were planted in 1971 and whose vineyards now covers 17 acres. Other examples are Leeds Castle, Kent, Renishaw Hall, North Derbyshire and Wiston Estate, West Sussex. The Royal family are involved, albeit at one remove – Pinot Noir, Chardonnay and Pinot Meunier varieties have been planted on a 3-ha site in Windsor Great Park, which is owned by the Crown Estate. Whether more stately homes and country houses will plant vines is unknown at present, but with a ready-made visitor market for their wines, more may appear in the future. Their wine could be made at a contract winery to limit initial outlay, but vineyard set-up costs and maintenance requirements still need to be considered.

Visitor centres

You do not have to have a special tasting room for visitors on tours, as a couple of oak barrels to stand the glasses on in the winery can be exciting and appealing to your guests. If you are keen to have a visitor centre or cellar door with a tasting room, though, then you will need to get planning permission and building regulations approval from your local authority. It is more complicated for listed buildings and conservation areas, but is slightly more straightforward if you want to convert an existing agricultural building. Planning guidelines require local authorities to help farms diversify by smoothing

Case study
The country house vineyard – Renishaw Hall, Derbyshire
www.renishaw-hall.co.uk

What do you add to the stately home that has everything? Well, why not a vineyard? Grapevines – and, of course, the wines they produce – are not only an additional attraction but are also a profit-centre in their own right, and many tourism-dependent country houses up and down the country have planted them. One of the most famous is Renishaw Hall in Derbyshire, ancestral home of the notoriously eccentric Sitwell family with a history going back to the early 17th century. Its vineyard was planted 40 years ago by the charismatic late Sir Reresby Sitwell, making it an impressive age for a UK vineyard.

When winemaker (and English Wine Project co-founder) Kieron Atkinson took over the running of all Renishaw's wine-related business during the summer of 2011, it was soon apparent that a number of improvements could be implemented easily to increase revenue from the vineyard and wine sales. Renishaw Hall and Gardens already attract in the region of 20,000–30,000 visitors a year, but opportunities were not being taken to raise awareness of the vineyard and its wine among this key audience. Kieron's first action, therefore, was to focus on how he could increase awareness of the vineyard and the wine, essentially a unique selling point of visiting Renishaw Hall, to people coming through the gate from April to October.

Kieron wanted the staff and volunteers who worked onsite to support the wine and vineyard more than they had previously done. The aim was for them to realise the potential of the Hall as well as improving the visitor experience. He organised training days and tastings so that everyone could get to know the wine.

Vineyard tours are also a revenue stream, but having tours available all day every day was not cost effective. Therefore he structured a package of tours for key months of the year to a minimum number of people. The tours averaged around 60 visitors a day on two tours. Any more than this and fatigue can set in for the tour guide.

the path of applications like this, but it can still be a lengthy process. Furleigh Estate, Dorset, for example, developed a cellar door and tasting room, and the conversion of the existing property took six months to complete.

Your business plan should include these plans and cover staffing costs, parking facilities, disabled access, hours of business, events, activities, income projections and initial financial outlay. Setting up credit card payment, staff payments and tax, business rate charges, VAT, staff training and building maintenance, as well as taking into account the requirements of future expansion, all need to be included in the plans. It's convoluted, but for many better-known vineyards and wineries it has all proved worthwhile in the end; other wineries that have visitor centres, wine shops and other facilities include: Chapel Down, Kent; Sharpham Estate, Devon; Three Choirs, Gloucestershire; Halfpenny Green, Staffordshire; and West Street, Essex.

Cellar doors and onsite shops do not just give you a place to sell direct to the customer, they can also offer food, accommodation and wine-related activities and products. Your employees are the ambassadors of your brand, so they need training in your product. Additionally, in line with your marketing strategy, branding should continue throughout the facilities with attention to buildings, signage and grounds. Family-focused activities and links with countryside events, such as nature trails that schools can benefit from, are worth considering, allowing for engagement with the local community. A very good example of this is at Rathfinny vineyard. There they have a nature trail which is officially classified as a permissive footpath around the estate and walkers can enjoy the Cradle Valley, vineyard, landscape and the wide variety of wildlife and fauna. Tours cost £20.

Café, tea rooms and restaurant

If you are considering an onsite café, tea room or restaurant then the first thing you will need is planning permission, whether it's to change the use of an existing building or to build an entirely new one. Different departments of the district council administer the planning and licensing applications – the local magistrates haven't been involved in alcohol licensing since 2003 – so there's always a risk of duplication. But alcohol licensing is a fairly straightforward business (see page 160); planning is a little more arduous!

There are several organisations to approach for help and guidance, and a good starting point is 'Run a Restaurant' **www.runarestaurant.co.uk**, which offers advice about setting up a restaurant, building and planning regulations, insurance, catering, health and safety, staff and business rates. Small business information, including legal advice, government grants and business funding and insurance, can also be sought from **www.smallbusiness.co.uk**. Business Link, which used to be so helpful, has now sadly been abolished. Talk to your accountant who will help you with the special VAT scheme, known as the flat rate scheme, for farmers who are not registered for VAT and consequently cannot reclaim the tax they pay on business purchases. However, they can charge and keep a flat rate addition of four per cent when they sell qualifying goods or services to VAT-registered customers. This is not VAT, but acts as compensation for losing tax on purchases. The flat rate addition can add up to an awful lot of money and is part of the business takings so should be included in sales.

If you decide to open a restaurant at the vineyard, it is important to know your local restaurants and coffee shops in order to understand the market for the local community and type of visitors to the region. This should be a major part of your business plan and, to attract funding, you need to know your potential local business competitors – both those that have succeed and those that have failed. Accommodation in the area is also relevant information for potential customers of the restaurant. This information will contribute to decisions such as your menu, hours of business, size of the restaurant, type of staff required, food suppliers and branding.

Vineyards and wineries with a restaurant on the premises will also find that they are a special kind of setting, with a romantic appeal to consumers and corporate entertainers that can be put to good use in otherwise slack periods. Of course there's the functions market –

Case study
Tours and tastings – Bolney Wine Estate, East Sussex
www.bolneywineestate.com

Tours and tastings are among Bolney Wine Estate's main income streams, vital not only as a cash-flow generator but also as a marketing tool for the vineyard itself and a means of educating the public about English wine more generally. They offer a variety of tours.

Grand Gourmet Tour: £42.50 per person – a comprehensive tour of the vineyard and winery, a tutored tasting of five of their award-winning wines and a charcuterie-style lunch (approximately 3½ hours).

Sparkling Afternoon Tea Tour: £34.50 per person – a comprehensive tour of the vineyard and winery, a tutored tasting of four of their award-winning sparkling wines and afternoon tea (approximately 2½ hours).

Taster Tour: £16.00 per person – a tour of the vineyard and winery and a tutored tasting of three of their award winning wines (approximately 1½ hours).

Drop-On Tour: £10.00 per adult, £3.00 per child – a 45 minute guided tour and tasting with two wines and juice for children.

The guides stay with their group throughout the whole tour to create a personal relationship, and they have to learn that customers come to the estate with certain expectations that the experience has to match up to. Guides also have to be ready for criticism and accept that not everyone is going to be full of praise or a delight to be with.

Although Bolney Estate is one of the pioneers of English winemaking, it was some time before it developed its own licensed café and shop, which account for more than a half of the estate's sales.

Even though it was only a question of extending an existing building, there were many planning delays arising from the requirement to address the legitimate concerns of neighbours, especially regarding September when the harvest brings visitors thronging to the vineyard.

and thank goodness for the 1994 Marriage Act! (See page 165) – but vineyard restaurants can also offer more imaginative events such as cookery courses, food and wine matching courses, guest chef nights (a particularly good promotion since your guest chef attracts diners and in return you promote his or her own venue – Camel Valley once hosted a fish barbecue prepared by double Michelin-starred chef Nathan Outlaw), guest cuisine nights, guest cuisine clubs, anything, in fact. Simply because of its location, your venue has a special appeal for you to exploit. An increasingly popular way of increasing awareness of your wines is to hold a 'Meet the Winemaker dinner' and match your wines to courses on the menu. (This is also a great promotion for supporting restaurants and gastropubs that stock your wines.) Check out the competition if you can: Highdown Vineyard, West Sussex, has a tea room in a converted barn; Jabajak Vineyard, Carmarthenshire, offers an à la carte menu in its four bistros; and Wyken Vineyard, Bury St Edmonds, Suffolk, has a vineyard restaurant in a beautiful 14th-century barn. Hattingley Valley vineyard, Hampshire, organises a range of diverse events and entertainment options for corporate functions. Its tasting room can provide a venue for an informal reception, conference or sit-down meal for up to 24 guests.

Alcohol licensing

The Licensing Act 2003 that came into force in 2005 took the alcohol licensing function away from local magistrates and awarded it instead to district and borough councils. The important provision of the Act for our present purposes was to split alcohol licences in two, so you now have to have separate personal and premises licences.

The personal licence
Ill-informed critics at the time claimed this merely added another layer of bureaucracy to an already growing pile; in fact, it did away with the cumbersome system of Transfer Sessions and Protection Orders. It is a widely-held misconception that all staff serving or selling

alcohol must hold a personal licence, although premises licensed to sell alcohol must have a designated premises supervisor who is a personal licence holder. Anyone who does not hold a personal licence must be authorised to sell alcohol by a personal licence holder. Applicants must be 18 or older, and once granted the personal licence is valid for ten years.

The licensing of individuals unconnected to any premises has two key advantages: it allows personal licence holders to migrate easily from one venue to another and, more important for our purposes, it also means that you can hold a personal licence without owning or operating a licensed premises, which is why you must have one. Possession of a personal licence allows you to hold up to 12 open days a year on your premises by submitting an application for a Temporary Events Notice, and to retail alcohol on other occasions such as farmers' markets in unlicensed venues. You can hold the licence for a third-party's event too, an agricultural show or community event, for instance, where you want to set up a stall to show off (and sell) your wares.

The personal licence is issued by your local council for a nominal fee. Before you apply, though, you'll need a National Certificate for Personal Licence Holders, and to get one of those you need to attend a one-day training course which has a 40-question multiple choice exam at the end. This will cost about £400. The British Institute of Innkeeping accredits some 500 training providers who run courses at over 5,000 locations all over the country – to find one, visit **www. bii.org**. The sheer number of training providers means you can shop around for the cheapest, but before enrolling do make sure that they actually teach the one-day course as well as the National Certificate in Licensed Retailing course. Not all of them do. To gain a personal licence you will also need a Disclosure and Barring Service check. Your local authority's alcohol licensing department should give you an application form before you apply for the licence itself. It's important to note that a personal licence alone does not allow you to sell alcohol online, but the virtue of getting a personal licence under your belt fairly early on is that once it's done, it's done. You can apply for a premises licence when you need one secure in the knowledge that at least one hoop has already been jumped through.

The premises licence

One difference between the 2003 Licensing Act and the 1964 Act that went before is that the law today requires licensees to be much more public-spirited than they used to be. Not only must they understand and swear to uphold public policy on alcohol-related disorder, protection of minors and so on, they also have to consult the police and fire services as well as the local community, who will all have a say on any conditions the local council might decide to impose.

In the short term, this is just another chore for licensees. On the one hand, getting a new licence or having an existing one varied is far more costly and time-consuming than it used to be. On the other hand, though, it's also far more permanent in that you only have to jump through the hoops once, because the Act also abolished the requirement to renew your licence at the annual Brewster Sessions. So once you've got it, you're on a much more secure footing than you used to be. Provided you respect the terms of your licence, it's hard for the police or neighbours to get it revoked or even reviewed. You've filed your flight-plan, as it were, in exhaustive detail and everyone concerned has had a chance to suggest alterations and restrictions. Everything has been openly negotiated and agreed, and as long as you stick to the operating schedule that the council has approved, nobody (in theory, at least...) has anything to complain about.

As mentioned above, modern licensing procedure is principally about consultation and ensuring that you understand your responsibilities. There's a fearsome-looking 16-page form to fill in, but if you download it from your local council's website and give it a thorough read you'll see that much of it isn't relevant to you. That's one of the (admittedly slight, in this case) drawbacks to the new one-stop licensing procedure: a single form has to cover every licensable activity including showing films, putting on plays, promoting boxing matches and so on, which makes it a pretty bulky document. (By the way, and although the form doesn't say so, the section regulating 'performance of dance' specifically excludes folk dancers.) But most

VINES DIRECT LTD

NEW VINEYARD ESTABLISHMENT

SITE SELECTION & SITE ASSESSMENT: Correct choice of site is vital in the UK's northerly winegrowing climate.

VINEYARD DESIGN: Design of your trellis system and density of plantation is offered as a standard part of our service.

PRE-PLANTATION ADVICE: All advice and organisation of soil & site preparation works.

GRAPEVINE SUPPLY: All vines sourced through one partner nursery, Proven vine establishment over many years.

VARIETIES, CLONES, ROOTSTOCKS: All combinations created to suit your vineyard site and target wine styles.

PLANTING: Planted by GPS guided machine, accurate to within 8mm.

TRELLIS MATERIALS: We supply everything, sourced direct from the factory to ensure lowest possible prices!

YOUR VINEYARD WILL BE IN THE GROUND FOR 40 YEARS. GET IT RIGHT FIRST TIME, WITH DUNCAN MCNEILL AND VOLKER SCHEU OF VINES DIRECT LTD.

CONTACT **DUNCAN MCNEILL** ON **07972 668370**
OR EMAIL **DUNCAN@MVM.UK.COM**

Capatex cloches improve yield and profitability

Rondo unprotected

Capatex Cloche installation

Rondo with Capatex Cloche

- Simple installation with 4-5 year expectancy
- All components included
- Yield increase of 9T/ha and over recorded due to larger berries and bunches*
- Yield increase of 3-5T/ha covers the Capatex Cloche investment*
- Rain protection shown to be more effective than fungicide spraying*
- Vineyards sprays likely reduced to two, at flowering and bunch closure.*
- Temperature increase under cloche up to 5C.*

Installation before bud break is recommended for optimal yield
Please call to discuss cloche trials, range of bird & insect nettings & mulches

Capatex Ltd.   0115 9786111   peter@capatex.com
Purchase Capatex Agro products on line at www.g-tex.co.uk
*Results based on trials, full results available on re

Vineyard Supplies

Trellis accessories, posts, wire, tying-in materials, clips & tools

Foliage Wire Spreaders

Bezinal® Wire

New Mage tying tool

GT Products Europe Ltd
Unit 14 Ford Business Park, Ford Lane, Ford, West Sussex BN18 0UZ
01243 555 303   sales@vineyardsupplies.co.uk
www.vineyardsupplies.co.uk

HORSEPOWER UK LTD

Address: Unit 2, Owens Court Farm, Selling, Faversham ME13 9QN
Telephone: 01233 226284 Email: sales@horsepoweragri.co.uk
www.wannersprayers.co.uk

KGR 45 2 ROW SPRAYER
Trailed two row air assisted sprayer, Twin Axle, choice of tank sizes.

TRAILED TOWER SPRAYER
K SERIES:
Trailed orchard style sprayer with a slightly narrower and taller tank than the N series. Full range of fan and tower attachments.

GERMAN, FAMILY OWNED COMPANY PRODUCING A HUGE RANGE OF SPRAYERS.

• BOTH MOUNTED AND TRAILED

• MULTI ROW SPRAYERS

• TANK SIZES FROM 200 TO 4000 LITRE

• ALL WITH GALVANISED CHASSIS

DA28 MOUNTED SPRAYER
D SERIES HITCHED SPRAYERS:
High-performance sprayer for modern plant protection – flexible use, adjusts optimally to crop and excellent spray coverage.
Tank sizes from 300 litres to 600 litres

  Landini   NSTS   WARWICK   EMILY   efco   McCORMICK

Vine Care UK

The UK's leading provider of vineyard labour

Offering the complete package, including:

- VINEYARD MANAGEMENT & CONSULTANCY
- TRELLIS INSTALLATION & REPAIR
- TRACTOR AND MACHINE OPERATORS
- CONTRACT SPRAYING SERVICES
- PRUNING & TYING DOWN
- BUD RUBBING
- CANOPY MANAGEMENT
- HARVEST SOLUTIONS

These are carried out by a dedicated and experienced team which includes tractor drivers and spray operators together with supervisors to oversee operations on a daily basis.

With many years' experience working in vineyards in England our team brings with them not only the essential skills required but a first class work ethic second to none – as clients will testify!

Whatever your viticultural needs, Vine Care UK can provide them!

For more information contact
Paul Woodrow-Hill (BSc Hons Wine Science)
Tel: 07811 613141 / 01243 210241
paul@vinecareuk.com

www.vinecareuk.com

Plumpton College Wine Centre

PLUMPTON COLLEGE

EST. 1926

The UK's centre of excellence in wine education, training and research

plumpton.ac.uk/courses/wine

University of Brighton

of it isn't concerned with alcohol licensing at all and need not concern you, and the trickier sections – such as those to do with carrying out the council's licensing objectives – will have been covered in the training course you completed when you got your personal licence.

The form, then, is fairly simple – you shouldn't need a solicitor to help you fill it out, and it should only take you a day or at most two. But the form is only the last part of the application process. You will also need to advertise your application in the manner prescribed by the licensing authority (which is not a new requirement); you will need to submit an accurate and intelligible plan of the premises, although hiring a proper draughtsman to do it probably won't be necessary; and you will need to submit copies to the 'responsible authorities' (fire, police and so on) as stipulated by the licensing authority. Just as important as correctly observing the formalities is to consult as widely as possible in advance, both with neighbours (and the term 'interested parties' includes nearby schools and businesses as well as residents) and with the 'responsible authorities' and the council's licensing officers. As with your planning application, if you do your homework thoroughly the application you finally submit should be bomb-proof.

The key to dealing with council licensing officers, as with HMRC and planning officers, is to be calm, rational and friendly, and not to regard them as jobsworths to be either bamboozled or placated or both. If treated with respect they can be – and indeed most of them want to be – extremely helpful, and can give you the advice that makes sure your application succeeds. They can suggest ways in which the four main licensing policy objectives can be met, many of which you may not have thought of. They will give you many invaluable tips, such as how to present the general description of the premises (section 3 of the application form) and the more detailed operating schedule as flexibly as possible, so you don't have to keep varying your licence whenever you want to try something new. They will have issues of their own to raise, too – you might, for instance, be in or near an area where public drinking is prohibited, and they may ask what steps you propose to deter customers from buying takeaways to drink in the street. (The best answer to this is to stress that your shop, if you have one, won't be selling cheap cans of lager or cider but extremely expensive bottles of top-quality and very expensive wines – although once you've made this commitment you will be bound by it.)

They may very well also want to know what provisions you have in mind for parking, toilets, noise abatement, control of numbers and public disorder should you be hoping to run on-site open days. Going into this kind of detail may seem a bit previous, but most of it will already have been drawn up and thoroughly worked through in your planning application. And it's just as well to have considered such matters as site layout, advance publicity and limiting numbers even at this early stage anyway because the value of possessing a site that's licensed to do pretty much anything is that as your business evolves, you can do… well, pretty much anything.

Food, drink and music festivals

Local food and drink festivals have grown in popularity across the country and are perfect places to introduce people to your wines, which can be purchased by the glass or the bottle. There may be an initial outlay for a stall, but this could be shared with another local winery to reduce costs. Cornwall, Kingston in Surrey, Manchester, Colchester, Nantwich, Exeter, Horsham, Ludlow and Bristol, to name only a few of the many throughout the country, hold local festivals. New Hall Vineyards near Maldon, Essex, has a dedicated English Wine Festival and Open Day for two days in late summer. It includes children's activities, wine tastings and tours, local food, fire-eaters, trailer rides and local craft stalls. The website **www.farma.org.uk** promotes farmers markets across the country and in addition, **www.thefestivalcalendar.co.uk** lists UK food and drink festivals free of charge.

The last word on the subject should go to Nick Mosley, Brighton and Hove Food & Drink Festival Director, "Food festivals are one of the most important ways for UK wineries to expose domestic consumers to English wine. Even in Sussex, an important wine-producing region of the south east, there is a huge lack of knowledge of local wines within the local population. Food festival events allow wineries to showcase their product to multiple demographics in terms of age, spend and wine knowledge. Intimate engagement between the business and the consumer, and the local hospitality industry, creates an important lasting impression that influences future wine purchasing. Brighton's food festival is unique, in that the organising committee consists of a group of volunteers from across the food and hospitality industry. Hence the commitment to promoting good, local food to residents and businesses spans not only the festival period but the entire year. Without a doubt, getting Sussex wines into more local retailers, bars and restaurants is a key objective of the organisation".

Weddings and civil ceremonies
Vineyards can be beautiful and magical settings for weddings and civil ceremonies, either as a location for the reception or, since the 1994 Marriage Act, for the actual marriage as well. Full event strategy and planning is part of a strong business plan to maximise income from the vineyard. For wedding licences to perform marriages, you need to apply to the Home Office via **www.gov.uk/government/publications/guidance-on-registering-a-venue-for-civil-marriage-and-civil-partnership**. As a wedding reception host, though, you and your restaurant manager (or your contract caterer, if you don't have a restaurant or if you do have a restaurant but only a bistro-sized kitchen) have to be real sticklers. It's the bride's big day to the nth degree, and every tiny detail has to be right. Room capacity, changing facilities, the state of the furniture and, of course, the quality and presentation of the food are all your responsibility but you need to be just as confident of the assiduity and punctiliousness of your outside contractors – marquee hire firms, functions florists, photographers, the band/DJ and the agency you hire your waiting staff from all have to be utterly reliable. It can also be useful to work with local hotels if your vineyard does not have accommodation available on-site, which in itself creates another opportunity. Here you are at the centre of a network of local catering and functions-related businesses, dishing

out contracts and business with a generous hand. Ask not only what you can do for them, but also what they can do for you!

Art exhibitions

The visitors' centre makes a very attractive and popular exhibition space for artists and craft fairs. And if you have the right kind of venue, the sky really is the limit, vineyards have been chosen to create temporary art galleries using natural materials and local artists, sculptors and schoolchildren, creating a real bond with the local community. Giffords Hall near Bury St Edmunds, Suffolk, for instance, had a locally based, but internationally recognised, contemporary artist and a photographer exhibiting their work during its open weekend. Art work exhibited on the vineyard property can bring people who might otherwise not think of visiting and after negotiation with the artist, the vineyard can earn commission from any works sold.

Leasing vines/Rent-a-vine/Adopt-a-vine schemes

Adopt-a-vine schemes are utilised by a number of UK vineyards such as Pebblebed Vineyard, Devon **www.pebblebed.co.uk** and Chapel Down, Kent has an extensive lease-a-vine scheme **www. chapeldown.com**. Kent Vineyard, Colliers Green **www.kentvineyard. co.uk** have launched a rent-a-vine scheme; Ryedale Vineyard, Yorkshire **www.ryedalevineyards.co.uk** has a similar scheme, as does Seddlescombe Organic Vineyard, East Sussex **www.englishorganicwine.co.uk**. These schemes increase income for the vineyard and can help secure grape pickers for the harvest and these types of schemes can also be purchased via online gift websites like **www. buyagift.co.uk**. All the schemes are different and purchasers receive different benefits, but a 'Friends of the Vineyard' scheme can result in long term, loyal customers and additional regular annual income. It is important to have administrative assistance with these schemes and be confident that all the benefits of the scheme can be delivered successfully. Any vines in the scheme need to be marked on a vineyard map, then tagged in the vineyard with the name of the purchaser, and competitions, newsletters and discounts offered to scheme members. Regular contact must be maintained with members. Social network sites offer a good way to do this, as well as seasonal email updates. The crucial point to remember with any rent-a-vine scheme is to show to the purchaser that the scheme is value for money and benefits them, as well as the vineyard.

Concerts

If you see your vineyard as a venue (and if it genuinely has the potential to be a venue), promoting live events could become a serious sideline for you. Vineyard concerts – whether small or large, grand classical galas or cool modern jazz or even local folk nights, are extremely popular in many wine regions, especially in New World wine-producing countries such as Australia, the USA and New Zealand where, of course, the weather is rather more reliable than it is here.

Taking the simplistic hard-nosed view, if you forbid your concert-goers to bring their own bottles, your concerts present a wonderful opportunity to sell yours – and at the on-trade mark-up. That, of course, is on top of ticket sales and food sales. And there are dozens of ways of doing it. Want to spread the risk? Then don't do your own food: sell concessions instead, perhaps to a swanky society caterer or maybe to local artisan producers. Want free music? Make it a talent night, or a showcase for the local amateur orchestra and choral society or school orchestra and choir (they'll want to pass the hat and probably run a raffle, but that's all good publicity and will bring in their friends and relations).

Promotional events are not only potential money-spinners in their own right but also another wonderful opportunity to reinforce your brand message. The kind of act you put on, the style of catering, the dress-code (if any) required of your patrons, the level at which you peg your admission charge and the price of food and drink – these are all statements. Are you Glyndebourne or Glastonbury or somewhere in between? Wherever you position your events, that's where you've positioned your wine.

Business courses and conferences

Many vineyards offer themselves as charming venues for business courses, conferences and seminars. Denbies Estate, for example, has a purpose-built conference facility providing a complete range of versatile function rooms and facilities. It can be hired out for all occasions and can accommodate up to 500 delegates. Denbies Estate has hosted the International Sparkling Wine Symposium and offers themed evenings, murder mystery weekends and many other specialised events. This scale of facilities requires a large financial input and must be part of a sales and marketing strategy, which is not necessarily feasible or even desirable for wineries whose prime target for investment is a modern state-of-the-art-winery capable of producing world-class wine. It's worth remembering that, being a vineyard and winery, your conference facility has a competitive advantage over more mundane venues such as hotels and golf clubs.

Farms, cottages and B&B accommodation

Some vineyards come with an extra bit of property that can be converted to earn its keep as a self-catering holiday let. It might be a surplus-to-requirements farm cottage as at Camel Valley near Bodmin (which actually has two of them), or, as at Aller Hill Vineyard in Somerset, it might be a picturesque 18th-century barn that could be converted into a two-bed holiday let. Alternatively there might be space in the main house itself to turn a room or two into B&B lets as do Tiltridge Farm in Worcestershire, which produces Elgar wine, and Denbies Estate in Surrey. Rathfinny Vineyard offers historic buildings in the Cradle Valley and has been beautifully restored and extended to the highest standard, forming a beautifully appointed 'home away from home'. Holiday accommodation provides a useful second income revenue for many vineyards, but can involve considerable expense as well as the time-cost implied by building regulations, planning consent and building work.

Harvest parties

Harvest celebrations are a high point in the winemaker's year in vineyards and wineries around the world, but in the UK they are usually the exclusive preserve of the staff and pickers. An annual harvest party for local people, with local food for sale, entertainment and the vineyard's own wine would increase local awareness of the brand, gather home-grown support by encouraging brand loyalty and, if an entrance fee were charged, generate a bit of revenue.

Friends of the vineyard schemes

A membership scheme that is common in the arts world, especially theatres and art galleries, might easily be adapted to vineyards. These schemes can be implemented at a local level and tailored to individual business requirements to increase both income and brand awareness. It would require administrative organisation, but could provide event volunteers, grape pickers for harvest, increase revenue and local brand loyalty, and even be purchased as gifts for wine-lovers. 'Friends' could benefit from invitations to exclusive events, seasonal newsletters from the vineyard/winery, discounts on wine tastings, advance wine sales, discount on facility hire, invitations to wine auctions, discount in the onsite restaurant or a renowned local eatery. The scheme could be organised as a single or joint membership, in tiers with gold, silver and bronze memberships, or in conjunction with a local wine club or shop. An example of how this works is at Titchfield Vineyard **www.titchfieldvineyard. co.uk** where you can adopt a vine at £73 per year, join their wineclub for £20 per year for which you will receive an invitation to the vineyard, join them at the annual grape picking and you get ten per cent off all their wines when you order online.

Community vineyards

Community vineyards and urban grape growing are increasing in popularity, and these are increasing in numbers. Detailed below are some examples.

Forty Hall Community Vineyards This is a social enterprise which has established a new ten acre organic vineyard in north London. Run and managed by local people, the vineyard is the first commercial scale vineyard in London since the middle ages. The vineyard produces and sells quality English still and sparkling wines.

Situated on Capel Manor College's Forty Hall Farm, they are certified organic and dedicated to demonstrating environmentally sustainable farming and vine-growing practices. Volunteers are the vineyard's lifeblood, and they rely on their volunteers in every aspect of vineyard management and development. Volunteering opportunities in the vineyard are currently available on Wednesday mornings (9.30am-1.00pm) and the first Sunday of the month (10.00am-1.00pm). All volunteers are given induction training and the chance to access other training provided by the vineyard. For individuals looking to get into work or accredited training, there is advice and signposting to relevant services and openings.

Olding Manor (Lewisham Organic Vineyard) The Vineyard measures just 0.01hectares and is based on St Mildred's Road Allotments, just off the South Circular in London, SE12. When they first started out, Olding Manor originally produced vintages using imported grape juice, sourced from as far afield as France, Spain, California and Australia. But then 2007 saw the first run of bottles made entirely from scratch, with grapes kindly donated from a nearby grower. The establishment of the Urban Vineyard in 2009 saw the first home grown organic hand made Olding Manor vintage, with a full run of estate produced wine, from three hybrid varietals imported from Germany. Two whites (Phoenix and Orion) and a red (Regent). No chemicals are used in the growing of the grapes, and everything is done by hand. 2011 saw the vineyard reaching full production, producing around 120 bottles.They are now expanding into a commercial enterprise with Wildwood Vineyard, a smallholding vineyard located in East Sussex.

Warden Abbey Community Vineyard The community vineyard is a not-for-profit project which aims to provide social, health and educational benefits for Bedfordshire whilst providing a financially and environmentally sustainable future for the historic vineyard. They aim to produce award-winning, quality still white wines each year, supplemented by a sparkling blend when conditions favour this. Sales of the wine support the project's work and saving the historic vineyard for the community.

None of these projects have wineries attached to them, so may require contract winemakers to produce their wines. If there is a local community vineyard in your area you may wish to consider contacting them with regards to offering your wine-production facilities.

Chapter Nine

Co-products
and by-products

W ithout the benefit of generations of patient soil conditioning, stone-picking, ditch-digging and terracing
behind them, few UK vineyards spread from hedge to
hedge across the plots of land on which they sit as they might
spread from crest to crest across some Burgundian vale. In many
cases only one or two parcels of a hectare or two each on a much
bigger plot – a smallholding, in effect – are suited to viticulture,
and the landowner is left with the problem of deciding how to
wrest a contribution to his livelihood from the rest.

Now small-scale viticulture, especially if you also make and sell
your own wine, is a pretty labour-intensive business. And it's not just
the toil in the vineyard that fills up the hours; this being an activity that
involves agriculture and alcohol – two of the most regulated areas
of endeavour in the Western World – it demands hours of toil in the
office too. So if you're looking at a complementary activity to
sweat those spare hectares it wants to be just that, complementary, using the same skills, the same tools and the same equipment, and as far as possible filling in the same forms for the
same officials.

And that's why so many UK wineries today either make cider on
the side or have done in the past. Perhaps the most prominent is
Biddenden, which is better known in its home county of Kent for its
cider than for its wine. The long-gone and much-lamented Merrydown (the liquid that bears that label today is no relation to the original,
being concocted in a factory in Belgium) was another. In poor years
when the grapes disappointed, Shawsgate used to make a crisp, dry,
pleasingly acidic single-varietal from Bramleys, as well as an apple
dessert wine of German heritage. Today Fenny Castle wines and Tor
Cider are the product of one and the same enterprise; Ludlow
Vineyard makes both wine and cider, and there are many others.

Orchards and vines

As long ago as 1120 William of Malmesbury wrote that the Isle of Thorney near Ely was so thickly planted with orchards and vineyards that it resembled an earthly paradise; and while in our patchy climate vines will only thrive on the very best ground, apple trees are much hardier and will flourish very nearly anywhere. If you are lucky enough to find yourself in possession of ten or 12 hectares in the Mendips, say, you might very easily find some nice south-facing, well-drained moderate slopes that are ideally suited to vines, some slightly chillier and shadier flat bottoms that will support a splendid cider orchard and some scrubby and exposed tops fit for nothing but a few sheep or, better still these days, camelids that can see the winter out on the hay you grew under your apple trees in summer.

But what sort of apples to plant? Two or three cider varieties to pollinate each other and produce a balanced blend of juices is the obvious answer. Britain's 300-odd cider varieties fall into four categories – sweet, sharp, bittersweet and bittersharp – depending on their proportions of acid, sugar and tannin, but perfectly good ciders can be made of dessert and cooking apples, and there are many multipurpose varieties such as Egremont Russet, Ashmead's Kernel and Kingston Black that perform brilliantly in all three roles. The key thing, though, is that they should be lates; you can pick those old cider standbys Dabinett and Yarlington Mill and many other less well-known types such as Chisel Jersey, Sweet Alford and Hereford Redstreak in late October/early November and leave them until December before milling and pressing. Late picking means that you need not start cidermaking until your grape harvest – which is, after all, the main event – is safely out of the way.

The two crops, then, live side by side very happily, the vines on the better ground, the apple trees on the poorer, even their harvests dovetailing rather than overlapping. They have much else in common besides. Soil management and conditioning, grafting on to rootstock, protecting and pruning the saplings, all the different aspects of canopy management, coping with fluctuating labour requirements – everything you do to a grape, you do to an apple (but you do it up a ladder).

The cidermaker's year

Here, then, to convince you even more strongly, is an outline of a cidermaker's year, starting once the crop is milled, pressed, pitched and put to bed.

Winter is a time of patience. There's nothing to do in the cidery but leave the yeast to its business. Out in the orchards, though, there's plenty of work. Once the leaves are fallen, it's time for pruning – a vital task in preparation for next year's crop. All the apples, not just those at the top of the tree, need sunlight. They need air, too, to dry them after rain, and space to minimise the spread of mildews and moulds.

Spring is blossom time, when the orchard froths with pink and white. Beekeepers with their hives are welcome springtime visitors to the orchards: the blossom provides a welcome breakfast for the bees, which in return do the essential work of pollination. Beautiful though blossom-time may be, it's a time of anxiety as a single late frost could forestall the harvest by killing the blossom – hence the expression 'nipped in the bud'.

Given a temperate spring, the cidermaker can afford to relax somewhat in the summer months and watch the apples swell. It wasn't always thus. Country lore gives St Swithun's Day, 15 July, as the date when early sweets might be ripe enough to pick to make a light table cider that ought to be ready for Christmas. But ideally you want varieties that ripen after the grape harvest is picked and pressed and safely in its fermenter. You are a winemaker first and foremost!

Even with no earlies to pick, summer can't be entirely given over to relaxation. Apples aren't the only organisms to burgeon in the sunshine; pests love the summer as much as the fruit does, and now is the time for spraying. Many modern growers have gone back to the old way of complementary planting, circling their orchards with hedgerows that provide habitat for predators that keep the pest population down. Still, some degree of spraying is still generally considered indispensable, even in organic orchards where insecticides based on natural plant extracts such as pyrethrum and nicotine, on sulfur and on metals including copper (harmful, but natural!) are permitted.

For owners of standard orchards (those with old-fashioned tall trees rather than modern bush trees), there's also some money to be made in summer when the grazing can be let out to stockbreeders. Sheep in particular thrive on orchard grass and windfalls; they also oblige the grower both by manuring the ground and by keeping down prolific plants, especially brambles, which would otherwise hinder the harvest.

Finally we come to autumn and the climax of the year – harvest. Picking apples in any quantity isn't easy, especially in old-style standard orchards where climbing to treetops with a basket is hardly an economic option. And waiting for the wind to do its work would be a long and unpredictable business, although windfalls can and are collected for cidermaking.

Traditionally, workers with long hooked panking poles simply shook the branches, while others collected the fruit as it fell. The apples would usually be gathered into heaps or tumps while saccharification continued. Tumping also dehydrates the fruit quite considerably, softening the flesh for easier milling and concentrating the sugars for a stronger cider. Then they would be floated in troughs to allow any leaves, twigs, staples, nails, pen-knife blades, loose change and insects to settle out and to allow the fruit to be inspected for rot (bruises are fine, but rot is not).

Modern orchards are harvested mechanically. They're planted in rows wide enough to allow the passage of a machine that clamps the trunks and then vibrates, rather than shakes, them – shaking loosens the roots and damages the trees. The first machine is followed by a blower that drives the fallen fruit from under the trees into the central lane, where it's picked up by a third machine that bears rotating rubber paddles that flip the apples into collecting bags. The three drivers collect far more quickly than three pickers ever could, and they don't get such bad backs either! If you're gathering manually, though, a plastic-bladed snow shovel is a great boon.

And so via mill and press to fermentation vat…

Cidermaking

So did any of that feel familiar? Most of it, probably. So should the process of cidermaking itself.

This is not the occasion to teach you how to make cider, partly because you already know the basics and partly because so many other sources of far more detailed information than would be appropriate here already exist both online and in print. Suffice it to say that the principal difference in the process is that no mere grape-crusher is strong enough to grind apples – tough little beggars with astonishing strength under compression – to the pulpy consistency required before they can be pressed, so you will therefore require a mill.

There are other subtle differences at various stages; take the question of wild versus cultured yeast, for example. The most traditional of cidermakers won't have a cultured yeast in the house; they maintain that nature provides perfectly good wild yeast, so why muck about? Others, however, want more control and prefer to introduce a wine or Champagne yeast. And once the primary fermentation is over there are makers who decelerate the whole process to a crawl first by dosing the cider with lime to precipitate the nitrogen and then by constantly racking the cider from one fermenter to another to keep the yeast population down. In France this process, called keeving, is used to produce exquisite sweet ciders of 2 or 3% ABV. Then there's blending. Few cider varieties are considered capable of producing a really good cider on their own and single varietals are therefore rare. Virtually all cidermakers blend, either by using a whole battery of laboratory equipment or by relying on their own instinct, experience and olfactory nerve, or just by crushing and pressing whatever fruit comes along, tipping it all into a tank and letting God get on with it. That seems to work, too.

Cider generally takes its time to ferment – November's pressing will take until the following May to be ready – and left to itself the fermentation will be thorough, leaving almost no residual sugar (which is why natural dry cider is such a Godsend to diabetics!) and at 6–8% ABV. But very dry cider can be very hard to drink, very astringent and even a little acetic, unless softened by a malolactic fermentation. Keeving, as described above, is one way of softening and rounding the palate but does leave residual sugar in its wake. Many cidermakers, even some of the most diehard traditionalists, choose therefore to use either an artificial sweetener or a natural fruit-derived polyol such as Xylitol or Sorbitol.

Cider is a perfect candidate for the méthode champenoise treatment, which in the context of modern English and Welsh winemaking is potentially very valuable, as we shall discover.

Income from the orchard

There are various ways you can make money from your bit of orchard, but your primary business is your wine; and in a shady orchard with the crimson globes of ripe apples winking through the dappled green canopy and a glass of cool cider fresh from the vat in your hand, it's terribly easy to lose focus. So let's be brutal.

First things first. You are allowed to make and sell up to 7,000 litres of still or sparkling cider and/or perry of up to 8.4% ABV absolutely free of duty. (see Sections 3.10 and 3.12 of HMRC Notice 162.) Do not, however, exceed 7,000l or you will have to pay duty on your entire output. Do not try to flavour your cider with gooseberries, lavender, rhubarb or any of the other fruits currently fashionable, or any other flavouring including honey, either, or it becomes liable not to cider duty but to wine duty! The rates of duty as set by the March 2016 budget are still to 7.5 per cent and sparkling to 5.5 per cent' £38.87 per hl. Still, 7.5-8.5 per cent, £58.75 per hl. Sparkling 5.5-8.5 per cent, £268.99 per hl! (This was after the Italians complained that the makers of Lambrini sparkling 'perry' were passing it off as Lambrusco, and that there should therefore be no tax differential between the two, to which our government instantly acceded.)

At roughly £2.50 a litre wholesale, your duty-exempt 7,000l should earn you £17,500 net, although you can increase your margin by bottling it in 9,200 nicely-dressed 75cl drawn-cork bottles, so that it looks like a nice Sauvignon Blanc, rather than in 500cl crown-cork bottles so that it looks like lager; £23,000 as opposed to £17,500 gross with luck, and using 4,800 fewer bottles, labels and closures. And here is where the méthode champenoise makes the whole venture worthwhile. If, like most English and Welsh winemakers these days, you are already concentrating on naturally sparkling wines, then you or your contract winemaker already have the equipment and the expertise to make naturally sparkling cider or perry. At £4–£5 a bottle wholesale, duty-free, that's a gross yield of £36,000–£46,000; and of course any you sell directly through your own shop and website will earn you twice that.

To yield 7,000l of juice you would need 15–20 tonnes of apples, depending on the year, which would be the average crop of about 0.5ha of bush trees or 1.5ha of standards. The density of bush trees can be as much as 600 per ha, that of standards maybe 100; so you need about 300 trees at £20 each to buy and plant. Your £6,000-worth of trees, if on a vigorous rootstock, should start yielding a worthwhile crop in less than five years and come to full production in less than ten. Your input costs are not going to be huge and the big jobs – the pruning, spraying and picking of 300 trees – can probably be carried out by your existing workers immediately after they've completed the same tasks in the vineyard. Apart from the pickers, in other words, they're on the payroll already.

Winemaking and cidermaking, then, really are complementary. Using the same skills, the same workers and the same equipment, high-end cidermaking can be a real boost to a vineyard's turnover. But the two activities can also work together to increase efficiency and sustainability.

Charcoal

One thing that everybody who reads this book will have in common is a visceral abhorrence of waste. A hatred of seeing perfectly good things being thrown out and effort being squandered must be one of the character traits that drives people to seek sustainability in the first place; to such people, the tangle of lopped shoots and branches left over after the winter pruning must be like a red rag to a bull.

Most vignerons would simply rake the prunings into a heap and strike a match. That's a terrible waste even if you don't have that impressive a heap; and if you have the prunings not only of your vineyard but of your orchard as well – especially if there are diseased branches or even whole trees to dispose of, if you haven't dealt with your Christmas tree yet and if you've been doing other bits and pieces of winter tidying around the garden – then you have potentially a useful amount of charcoal.

Charcoal is wonderfully versatile stuff. Banked up on the wood-burning stove last thing at night, it'll ensure there's still a rosy glow when you come down in the morning. If you can make commercial quantities of it, bag it up and sell it in your shop in summer. A local chef might be glad of a regular supply, since both vine and apple-wood charcoal confer highly distinctive flavours and aromas and are greatly sought after. One day it might even generate the steam to heat up your very own pot-still, but we'll come to that.

But it's as a soil conditioner that charcoal displays its almost magical powers. Its filtration properties are well-known – it traps nutrients that would otherwise be leached away by rainwater, thereby improving the soil's fertility. It fixes greenhouse gases including carbon dioxide, nitrous oxide and methane. It's a source of slow-release nitrogen. And being alkaline it reduces soil acidity and inhibits the growth of club root. (A caveat here, though – fruit and potatoes actually prefer fairly acid soil.) Even the ash (used sparingly, though as it's even more alkaline than the charcoal itself) is a good soil improver, especially as a source of potassium. It can be added very gradually to a compost heap or raked directly into the soil in winter, when the pervading damp will dilute its alkalinity.

Turning that heap of cuttings and prunings (and the Christmas tree!) into this wonderful substance is a simple process, but like many simple processes, it's not necessarily easy because it depends so much on your own judgment and experience – which, of course, you haven't got yet. But this is the theory and it's up to you to put it into practice.

Charcoal is no more than wood with all the water and volatiles driven out by combustion and the remainder reduced to almost pure carbon by a slow no- or low-oxygen burn. There are several ways of doing this and here's the simplest.

First find an old oil drum or a big metal bin with a very tight-fitting lid. Make a hole a few inches from the bottom just big enough for an air inlet made of a piece of pipe a foot or so long, with a bung that will plug it exactly. Pack the drum as tightly as humanly possible with your prunings, splitting any larger pieces into battens of no more than two or three inches thick. For an accelerant you can use a piece of old rag soaked in used cooking oil, splashing a little more accelerant into the prunings. Light the rag, chuck it in and stand well back. As the fire takes hold, what you'll see first is a thick cloud of steam as the water content (which can be as much as 40 per cent of the weight of fresh cuttings) is driven off. After a while, depending on how green your wood is, the steam will be replaced by dirty brown smoke as the fire heats up and the various volatiles evaporate.

Once the smoke and flame have died down, the third stage begins. First plug the air inlet at the bottom of the drum as snugly as you can; then clap the lid on to the drum and make it airtight using either a clamp or handfuls of soil or both. Be exact about this – any air that gets in could re-ignite the flames and you'll be left with nothing but ash. Now all you have to do is leave the charcoal to itself; after two or three hours, perhaps longer, the drum will cool down and you can unseal it and see how thorough your burn was. Not perfect, but any wood that hasn't carbonised will find another use elsewhere.

Pomace

If you mill and press a lot of fruit, you're going to be left with a lot of pomace. Apples and grapes typically contain 65–80 per cent juice, but the most efficient press in the world won't extract all of it. If you press 100kg of apples (the likely yield from a medium-sized tree in an average year), you could be left with 30kg of moist squidgy brown stuff. It may look like trash to some, but in reality it's full of useful substances and is far too good to waste.

For most of the world's big industrial juice and cider makers, who of course have millions of tonnes of the stuff on their hands, safe disposal is actually a major problem. In Britain there's a long tradition of using it to make pectin, the gelling agent that sets your jam and marmalade and has 101 other industrial uses as well. In fact HP Bulmer, Britain's largest cidermaker, was for decades also Britain's largest producer of pectin.

But the most obvious use for it, if you're only pressing small quantities of fruit, is to compost it and very good compost it makes, too. It's packed with micronutrients, it generates loads of nitrogen as it breaks down and its fibre content – typically 60 per cent or more – makes it great for improving soil structure. Two tips, though, don't chuck it straight on to the heap from the press, as it will still be fairly moist and quite acidic. Mix it with an equal volume of dried leaves or shredded cardboard or newspaper first. And when you do add it to the heap, bury it deep as its starch and sugar content of up to 20 per cent (although less if you've made ciderkin) is a magnet for wasps.

If you're pressing in large quantities, pomace makes great mulch. A 7–8cm layer, partially dried before being spread around new and tender plants, will help keep young root systems warm through the winter and, come spring, will suppress weeds. You can then either simply let it rot where it lies to release its nutrients into the soil, or rake it up and pop it into the compost.

If you have even larger quantities, your pomace is ideal as feed for livestock, either your own or a neighbouring farmer's; and in fact for some cidermakers, the income from sale of pomace as feed is the first buck they earn from their year's crop. Its principal constituent is fibre that humans can't digest but herbivores can, and on top of that there's the sugar and starch mentioned above and about 7-8 per cent protein as well as various micronutrients including vitamins. It can be fed straight to the animals, or dried on racks to help it keep; alternatively it can be used as a nutritious addition to silage. Some even make their own form of silage by packing their pomace fresh from the press into airtight drums, where its continuing chemical reactions generate enough heat to dry it out thoroughly.

There are other, less orthodox, uses for pomace. Mixed 50:50 with sawdust, it makes an effective growing matrix for mushrooms. Either fresh or dried and then rehydrated, it can be added to cake or cookie mixture and baked. And of course, if you have enough of it, you can always rehydrate it slightly, ferment it, press it and distil it as an eau-de-vie, which we shall come to below.

Distilling

The huge increase in the number of craft distilleries in Britain since the beginning of the century has been remarkable. There is now a baffling number of small-batch gins on the market, flavoured with anything from good old juniper to rhubarb; and in Scotland the gaps between old-established whisky distilleries are rapidly filling up with new ones.

It all started in the 1980s with two cidermakers, Bertram Bulmer in Herefordshire and Julian Temperley in Somerset, who were prepared to lock horns with stubborn authorities both at home and in the EU and who overcame enormous hurdles to get their respective ciders distilled. There was a bit of a lull after that, and the next batch of craft distillers to tackle Her Majesty's Revenue & Customs were mainly London-based gin rectifiers who didn't, and don't, actually distil their base spirit from raw ingredients but bought it in from old-established makers. Since then all kinds of things have changed: equipment costs have come down, there are consultants all over the place, HMRC has become almost affable and online retailing enables makers of very high-end consumer goods to bypass the established retail chain altogether.

This means that now is the time for winemakers to exploit the growing opportunity in the retail trade for their products in distilled form. The UK industry has already shown itself the equal of the French in quality sparkling wines, so why not in brandy?

We are not going to address the administrative complexities implicit in establishing your own distillery alongside your winery – we are merely going to spell out the potential a still creates for getting extra money out of your harvest and then direct you to our companion volume, *The Craft Distillers' Handbook*. Suffice it to say that these days

Case study
Extensive farming – Fenny Castle Vineyard & Tor Cider
www.fennycastlevineyard.co.uk

The Fenny Castle Vineyard story started in 2005 when James and Gill Cumming quit the rat race (he was in the print industry; she was a teacher) and bought the very run-down 5-ha Panniers Farm near Wells in Somerset.

The south-facing land was a mixture of rough grazing, scrubby coppice and ancient orchard that had all been neglected for many years, and although they had the idea of planting a vineyard almost immediately after they arrived, they spent the first years farming a small flock of Suffolk sheep, raising rare-breed pigs and building up a holiday letting business.

The idea was always to farm extensively rather than intensively in order to broaden their business base and maximise the potential of their smallholding; and as soon as it was feasible James went back to school, studying viticulture and winemaking for two years at Plumpton College in East Sussex. Finally, six years after they had moved in, and with the help of their pigs who cleared the brambles and broke the ground for them, James and Gill planted their first vines. By the time they'd finished in summer 2012 they'd planted 2,000 Bacchus, Ortega and Pinot Noir vines on two parcels of land totalling about a hectare and had also built their own small winery in which they make two méthode champenoise sparklers (one of them rosé) and two still Ortegas (one of them barrel-fermented).

But sheep, pigs, a holiday cottage and winemaking did not exhaust the resources either of Panniers Farm or of the Cummings. As soon as the wine business was more or less established they found a new way of diversifying and of getting more use out of their winery and winemaking skills: cidermaking. Their own orchard was simply too overgrown to harvest, but in the immediate area they found three unused orchards whose crop they could harvest; under the name Tor Cider they now make three single-orchard ciders and bottle-fermented sparkling dry, all of which are as well-regarded among connoisseurs as their wines.

you can equip a perfectly viable distillery for £25,000 or thereabouts, and that no special skills or even training are required to operate it.

One reason given by English winemakers for their reticence in jumping on the distilling bandwagon is simply that they don't grow enough grapes. This is true – but only to an extent. In bad years such as 2012 it is still worth picking the grapes, low in sugar, undersized and acidic as they may be, because they will produce the sort of wine that makes the finest brandy. Then there's the pomace. Your white pomace, rehydrated and fermented, can be distilled, as can the fermented pomace of your red wine. Your bottle rackings and the lees from your maturation tanks can be filtered and distilled. Blended together and watered down to bottle-strength, these spirits make marc or grappa. If your own supplies of pomace and lees are insufficient, you might pool your own stocks of potentially valuable waste-products with those of a neighbour or two, as many small French winemakers do. Then there's your cider – you may be selling the full quota of 7,000l of it duty-free qua cider, but you can make any amount on top of that to turn into cider spirit (not cider brandy or apple brandy – the French, who dominate the EU in these matters, insist that it's only brandy if it's made of grapes).

And after all that, you still have pomace nutritious enough for cattle-cake. Once you've extracted the nine to ten per cent ethanol content from the various fermented liquids in your still, you have gallons and gallons of pot ale that can easily be aerobically digested to produce biogas.

Hedgefruit

A commitment to sustainability, as noted above, necessarily implies a loathing of waste. And while a shelterbelt (or windbreak) is in principle just that – a shelterbelt – it's much more, too; it's almost a little farm in its own right. Before introducing any hedgefruit onto the vineyard, very careful consideration should be undertaken to ensure that you are not introducing any kind of vineyard pests such as Spotted Wing Drosophilia (SWD).

The foundation of your shelterbelts should be a dense thorn

with plenty of growth at ground level, especially the blackthorn that blossoms in March or even February to provide an early reviver for the bees and at the very end of the year produces the sloe. Sloes, of course, are most renowned for their power to transform gin. But left on the tree until nipped by frost they lose some of their bitterness and astringency and make very good jam and pie-filling.

If the thorn is the natural king of the hedgerow, it is attended by a whole court of fruit and nut trees that will also yield a worthwhile harvest.

Most stone fruits, but especially the rougher, less sophisticated varieties, are perfectly at home in the hedgerow and in some cases have graced shelterbelts for centuries. The cherry plum, like the blackthorn, blossoms early but bears a far sweeter fruit. Damsons, gages, the near-forgotten but astonishingly hardy bullace – their fruits are all equally suited to cordials, to liqueurs, to jams, jellies, pie-fillings and sauces. They can be pickled to make a form of umeboshi, and they are both delicious and nutritious dried.

Even discarded stones have their uses. They can be composted, although they take so long to degrade that they are best kept apart until they have begun to disintegrate. The process can be speeded up by keeping them in a bucket of water for a few months before adding them to the heap. They can be dried and burnt in the wood-burning stove or a biomass boiler, although they do make a lot of ash. They can be smashed to liberate the soft kernels, which can then be ground and cold-pressed to yield the kernel oils so highly prized both in the kitchen and in the making of cosmetics. Kernels steeped in gin or vodka also make a more than passable noyaux.

Alongside the various stone fruits, no orchard windbreak is complete without a few crab apple trees. They are great pollinators, and the fruits make a sharp jelly ideal with pork or game. The juice is particularly useful if you want to make cider but have only eaters and cookers in your orchard bcause they are high in the tannin and malic acid that dessert and culinary varieties lack. Both chemicals are antibacterials that will help your cider mature properly, while the malic acid should in time break down into the lactic acid that will make your cider smooth and mellow.

Hazel is another useful hedge plant – as well as their nuts, the trees provide good straight rods with a multiplicity of uses; and after eating the nuts, the dried shells make excellent kindling. Hazelnuts (and their relatives, cobnuts and filberts) are also so versatile in the kitchen that they're the cold-climate equivalent of the almond and they can be used fresh in salads and desserts, toasted in biscuits and confectionery, dried and chopped in stuffings and sauces, dried and ground in cakes and pastries, roasted, smashed and boiled with sugar in syrups and creams, even chopped and steeped in spirit as a basis for various liqueurs – there really is very little you can't do with them. Even the shells need not be discarded – first they make mulch, and then you can dig them into the compost.

Climbing roses, too, have a place in your hedge. When they're in bloom they just make the orchard a happier place to be for workers both human and apian, for their long flowering season (if you choose the right varieties, that is) will ensure a heavy crop of deliciously scented honey. But they have many culinary uses, too; the petals will make jam, syrup and rosewater, while fruits or hips are very high in vitamin C and will flavour jam, jelly, tisane, wine, mead and cider. You can make an infusion of rose petals and honey, too, a bucolic luxury not to be ignored.

Elder will appear in your hedge whether you want it to or not. It's very invasive and prolific and it has to be strictly controlled as, left to itself, it tends to take over. Once established, an elder can quickly grow to 7–8 metres tall or more, towering over and shading your vines, so be brutal with the loppers! It's not even that good a hedge plant, as the boughs only start appearing several feet up the trunk; and the wood is good for nothing but kindling. Nevertheless, both flowers and berries are very useful and versatile hedge products. The strongly-flavoured flowers that appear in June have a million-and-one culinary uses – cordial, elderflower champagne, jelly, fritters – and are becoming very popular as a botanical. The berries, like sloes, are rich in tannin and can make a wine that will not only keep for years, but will carry on maturing and improving as it does so.

Finally, a cautionary word about bramble. Apple and blackberry are natural companions in all manner of recipes from fruit pies and crumbles through to flavoured cider and mead, but the briar is both prolific and invasive, sending suckers underground to burst forth in unexpected and unwanted places. It is also incredibly resilient. It is possible, just, to eradicate blackberries completely with repeated applications of noxious chemicals or by digging out the rhizomes and crowns over and over again. But you will probably want to keep at least some blackberries, and you certainly won't want an orchard soaked in glyphosates or other herbicides. The only answer, then, is to mulch heavily wherever you don't want blackberries, and to nip off new shoots as they appear.

Poultry

Chickens and vineyards – and orchards too – go together like a horse and carriage. Chickens are descended from jungle birds and, despite the passage of countless generations, still feel more secure under a forest canopy, for which your vines and trees make a satisfactory substitute. In return for your care and attention they will oblige you not only with eggs and meat, but also with bonemeal and dung to add phosphorus and nitrogen to your soil and litter to swell your compost heap; they will also devour bugs and insects that would, left undisturbed, make a meal of your vines.

Keeping chickens can play as large or as little a part in the life of your vineyard as you want. Half-a-dozen bantams make a delightful addition to any backyard or suburban garden; not only will they provide a reasonable supply of eggs but, carefully managed, they do more good than harm to the garden itself. They generally get on well with household pets, and they generally become pets themselves. At the other end of the scale, hen-keeping can be one of the most intensive forms of agriculture allowed. EU regulations permit up to 2,500 free-range birds per hectare; in the UK the RSPCA recommends a maximum of 2,000. These maxima, of course, relate to fowl reared indoors on a fully commercial basis and are not really relevant to a mixed farm of a few hectares; nevertheless they suggest that if your patch of vineyard is your livelihood, then hen-keeping could easily become your second largest source of income after the wine itself.

Having said that, keeping hens on any sort of scale is extremely labour-intensive, and spare labour is the one thing the small vigneron is often short of. The coop really has to be dug out every two days, and although the litter makes a useful and plentiful mulch or, well-rotted, a very rich fertiliser, the more hens you have the bigger the job. By the same token, daily chores such as getting the flock in at night, feeding and watering it and collecting the eggs become more onerous the more numerous the fowl. Routine maintenance, too, is of critical importance – minor damage to coop or pen might not let the fox in, but rats, stoats and weasels are equally lethal and can easily squeeze through the tiniest gap. Nor can hens really be left to get on with their scratching and digging. Pests and diseases can spread through a flock like wildfire, and the best way to deal with them is by constant vigilance and prompt action. You have to spend time with your hens to keep abreast of their state of health. And finally, while the digging and scratching of a few birds is good for the garden, aerating the soil and eradicating pests, it might not be so welcome on a grander scale. The size of flock you can feasibly run, therefore, is a function of your time and space.

The question of breed is probably more important for the small hen-keeper than it is for the commercial chicken farmer, especially if egg sales are part of your income and you might benefit from having the unique selling proposition of an unusual, and perhaps endangered, breed. You will undoubtedly need to get advice from an expert before making what could be an expensive mistake here, but if you are limited for space you will probably find one of the feather-legged bantams suits you best. Feather-legged breeds tend to make less mess than their bare-legged counterparts, and bantams, although they require less in the way of space and fodder, lay eggs almost as big as a full-sized hen's. Another option that suits the sustainability ethos is to build up a flock of rescued ex-battery hens, which have the advantage of being about half the price of full-breed fowl (there are even charities that give them away free, although they expect a donation to cover their not inconsiderable costs).

Far less domesticated than chickens are guinea fowl. They don't come when they're called, they don't particularly like being handled and they generally prefer to roost in trees than in a secure coop, which makes them very vulnerable to predators (although they can be conditioned to using coops if you start training them young). On the other hand, they require very little feeding or other maintenance, they lay eggs that are small but very highly flavoured (but they almost always lay out, concealing their clutches in clumps of nettles and the like, so you need to keep an eye on the hen fowl to see where their favourite spots are) and the meat is more like game than domestic poultry. In fact, it even needs to be cooked like game, using pheasant recipes, as it can be very dry. As a bonus, their feathers are sought after by fly-fishermen and milliners.

Chapter Ten
Finance

Many are seduced by the romance of planting a vineyard and making their own wine, and while many succeed, many others fall by the wayside. The wine business is indeed romantic but like any other business it requires knowledge, financial acumen and hard work. Planting a vineyard is essentially farming; winemaking is an industrial process; and selling wine is marketing. So enjoy the view – who couldn't? – but keep a sharp eye on the bottom line too.

How much money will you need to make your wine? Well, how long is a piece of string? There are so many variables, and you can become involved in the wine industry on so many levels – it really depends on how much of the process you want to take on yourself and on what scale.

The industry in the UK is developing rapidly, with more qualified consultants and suppliers coming into the market, but that doesn't mean that prices for equipment and services are beginning to fall yet. Despite the increasing prominence of English sparkling wines, the UK is still only a tiny market for most of the suppliers you will be working with. Your choices will be limited to those companies that are prepared even to contemplate doing business in the UK. Some will flatly turn you down. You will not therefore have the bargaining power of a Champagne or Loire Valley winemaker when it comes to negotiating prices. Also, it is worth remembering that if you ask a supplier for a complicated quote for thermo-regulation, tanks, etc. and then take the information he has spent hours compiling for you and try to go to his competitors, word will get round, and you might find that original supplier will no longer wish to work with you. This may seem alien to the UK mindset of doing business, and may very well be illegal under EU law, but be aware that the winery and vineyard supply businesses all tend to know each other, and it pays to keep your suppliers happy. We are useful to them as a safety-valve market, but we are certainly not integral to their business. You will get further with goodwill than hard-nosed haggling.

This is not to suggest that you should be prepared to be ripped off – just go into negotiations with a firm dose of reality; it costs money for them to do business in the UK, and you will not get the same prices open to larger winemaking regions.

Planting a vineyard, building and equipping a winery, selling the resulting wine – all of these are separate businesses within themselves. You can merely grow and sell grapes; buy grapes and make wine; or buy bulk wines to bottle and sell. There are now some 'virtual winemakers' entering the UK market – they own no vines and have no winery but 'create' a label or brand under which to sell. They buy grapes and have a contract winemaker produce the wine without the need to ever see a vine, let alone prune one. It is a common business model in more established New World regions such as California. The risk is minimal – if there is a poor vintage with low yields, they only pay for the grapes they receive, while the grower has still incurred the same costs in running their acreage. Similarly, the winery taking the grapes under contract has to have capacity for the full projected yield (investment in tank space and other kit) but, again, if yields are low then the winery's revenue will be reduced. The biggest risks a virtual winemaker faces are not being able to source sufficient grapes or to sell his or her wine, and building a brand without having a place such as a vineyard or winery to pin it on can be tough.

You've decided on your wine style or styles. The costs are going to be determined by this – sparkling wine requires much more capital investment than still wine, and demands a longer period of patience before you will realise any potential return.

English still wines, selling at £10+ per bottle, are still perceived as expensive. By contrast, sparkling wine at £20 can look good value next to Champagne. The average retail price paid for still wine (from any country) is still around the £6 mark. Bearing in mind that nearly half of that is duty and VAT, and most of the rest goes to the retailer, there's not much room for a small-scale producer to make a profit. To persuade the consumer to more than double their average spend to buy an English still wine is a long shot. For this reason still wines are always going to have a limited market, restricted to consumers who are adventurous and prepared to spend a bit more money.

Sparkling wine, on the other hand, is viewed entirely differently – as a special occasion wine. The normal self-imposed restrictions on price paid are removed, and the consumer will pay much more for the perceived quality of English sparkling wine. Some basic research online and at Waitrose will show you what prices are currently achieved by English wines. All your costs are higher for sparkling, including duty, but the financial rewards can be higher still if you have the capital to invest for several years before you realise them.

Financial help available

There are various sources of funding, agricultural subsidies and business grants that are available to potential vineyard and winery owners, although rather less than there used to be. The South East England Development Agency (SEEDA), a body that had given enormous help to the fledging English wine industry, was wound up in 2012. There are many, many vineyards and wineries in the UK that would never have got off the ground without the matched grant funding from SEEDA; many others have upgraded their facilities and subsequently the quality of their wines thanks to these grants. This shortsightedness on the part of a government desperate to increase economic activity, in one of the few growing and vibrant rural industries the UK has, is depressing. But there are other avenues for funding if you look hard enough. Although the SEEDA funding has been cut off, it would be worth keeping in touch with Defra to be sure you don't miss out on any new grants that come on-stream.

The Prince of Wales not only operates the Prince's Trust for business grants and loans for under-30s, but he also has a lesser-known rural funding scheme, The Prince's Countryside Fund (**www. princescountrysidefund.org.uk**). There are quite tight criteria in terms of giving back to the rural community regarding amenities and jobs, but at least one vineyard is applying for the funding. The goals of the charity are:

- To improve the sustainability of British farming and rural communities, targeting the areas of greatest need.

- To reconnect consumers with countryside issues.
- To support farming and rural crisis charities through a dedicated emergency funding stream.
- Any candidate for funding under the scheme must meet at least one of the criteria.

There are also commercial loan and mortgage companies that specialise in the rural and farming industries; one example, although by no means the only option, is **www.fundingoptions.com**. The National Farmers Union **https://nfu.org** is also a great source of financial help and advice on straightforward banking issues as well as grants.

Basic farm payment scheme

At time of writing the UK has voted to leave the EU, but was facing a very long and involved process of actually untangling itself from the many and varied treaty obligations implied in membership. In the meantime, EU laws and regulations still hold good, so as a farmer you should still be entitled to the EU's Single Farm Payment Scheme – contact the Rural Payments Agency Customer Service Centre on +44 (0)345 603 7777 or CSC@rpa.gsi.gov.uk to find out your eligibility. More information can be found on **www.rpa.defra.gov.uk**.

Commercial vineyards of one hectare or more (so, not hobby vineyards!) can apply for the European Union's Basic Payment Scheme that in 2018 was £210 per hectare – so not a huge amount, but probably worth having. Payment is conditional on whether land management complies with the regulations detailed on the Defra website. Payments are not linked to production (although you have to be an active farmer, but environmentally friendly farming practices (known as cross compliance) are rewarded. There is a *BPS Handbook for England* with details of the scheme on the Rural Payments Agency website including information about eligibility and how to claim the subsidy.

It's an unbelievably convoluted scheme and any eligible UK vineyard that wishes to claim the subsidy must hold enough 'entitlements' to cover the land. One entitlement covers one hectare of eligible land. If you are buying land with a BPS entitlement you need to contact the customer service centre (see previous page) to register your business and obtain a Single Business Identifier before any entitlements can be transferred to you from the vendor, who will need to complete an RLE1 form and return it to the Rural Payments Agency by the deadline stated to claim SPS for the coming year. The minimum amount of land that can be claimed for under the scheme is one hectare.

Environmental stewardship scheme

Commercial vineyards registered on the Rural Land Register may be eligible for the Environmental Stewardship (ES) schemes managed by Natural England on behalf of Defra, as part of the Rural Development Programme for England.

ES is a government scheme that makes payments for good stewardship and management that improves the quality of the environment. Details are on the Defra website. There are three levels in the ES scheme: Entry Level Stewardship, Organic Entry Level Stewardship and Higher Level Stewardship. The main objectives of ES are to conserve wildlife biodiversity, maintain and enhance the landscape, protect the historic environment, promote public access and understanding of the countryside, protect natural resources, prevent soil erosion and water pollution and support environmental management of uplands areas.

ELS provides a straightforward approach to supporting the good stewardship of the countryside. This is done through simple and effective land management that goes beyond the Basic Payment Scheme's requirement to maintain land in good agricultural and environmental condition. It is open to all farmers and landowners. OELS is for organic and organic/conventional mixed farming methods, and is open to farmers registered with an organic certification body that are not in an existing organic aid scheme. HLS involves more intricate types of management, where land managers need advice and support, and agreements are tailored to local circumstances. HLS applications are assessed against specific local targets, and payments are offered when these targets are met.

All these schemes are found in more detail, including requirements for eligibility and application information, on the Natural England website, **www.naturalengland.org.uk**.

Vineyard costs

Agricultural land in the UK is much cheaper than in the classic, old-established wine regions. For comparison, a hectare of vineyard land in the Champagne region will change hands for a €1 million, a hectare of Napa Valley vineyard will cost $250,000, and a hectare of suitable land in the UK might only cost £25,000 (source: Savills Farmland Value Survey 2017). However, farmers and landowners with suitable sites for vineyards in the South of England are wising up to the fact that a sheltered, south-facing, free-draining slope at less than 100 metres above sea level is a fairly rare commodity, and have started asking higher prices. Strutt & Parker **www.struttandparker.com** is one estate agency that has taken an interest in vineyard-suitable land, having brokered many of the deals for Nyetimber's recent expansion across the south. It is involved with many new projects and the sale of existing vineyards.

Soil sampling is vital when considering a new site, and there are consultants who can do this for you. Expect to pay up to £300 a day for their time plus laboratory fees for the actual testing, although the cost will vary according to the number of samples. Prices can be requested from laboratories such as FAST **www.fastltd.co.uk**. Companies such as Vine Works **www.vine-works.com** and Vineyard Consulting **www.vineyardconsulting.co.uk** will undertake site assessments for a fee that can be negotiated according to location and size of the potential plot.

Once you've made your purchase of land you will need to prepare the soil for planting. You could hire a local farmer to do the preparation for you, or rent a tractor and the ploughing and harrowing equipment. You will never need a large tractor again once the vines are in, so it's not cost-effective to buy one.

Deer and rabbit fencing is almost obligatory in the UK if you want your baby vines to survive beyond their first year. Again, how much this costs will depend on the size of the area you wish to protect. Rabbits can also be prevented with grow-tubes, which also offer some protection against frost for young vines. Vine guards can cost 50p each. Badgers will also eat ripe fruit and so electric fencing may be required.

Machine planting is used on the majority of plantings although there are sites that due to either soil texture, climate during planting, site inclination and accessibility hand planting is the chosen option.

In 2018 due to the wet subsoils in the spring, particular attention was needed to the clay content on a planting site and its subsequent form below ground after the planting machine had created its planting furrow. Some owners like the idea of handplanting but need to understand with handplanting the plants tend to be planted nearer the surface with 'slit planting' and as a result these vines are highly vulnerable in drought years without expensive irrigation and in clay soils they need to be careful with augering holes in wet conditions as this can create soil vases in the soil.

The summer following the planting will see the need for trellising to be installed. This again will vary enormously in cost according to size, and you need to take into account your soil type. If you have solid chalk at 20cm below the surface, it will cost more to drive the posts in, and you may need sturdier posts at a higher cost as well. You should budget for £25–£30,000 per hectare on top of the price of the land to get established with vines and trellising. This should also cover maintenance and labour for the first two years before the vineyard becomes productive.

Selling/purchasing your grapes

If you decide that you just want to be a grape grower, then you can sell your grapes as a cash crop. Alternatively, you might wish to enter the market at this point and buy grapes from a vine grower. Still wine varieties can typically fetch around £1,800 a tonne, while sparkling varieties can command £2,500, but the actual price paid can go down if good ripeness is not achieved, and up if a better balance between sugar and acidity is realised.

Case study
Funding expansion mutually – Chapel Down Vineyard
www.chapeldown.com

Chapel Down of Tenterden, Kent, is one of England's oldest-established vineyards and wineries. When it started up in the 1970s, German-style still white wine dominated the English industry and that was what Chapel Down produced. Since then the company, in line with the industry as a whole, has shifted its focus to top-quality, high-value sparkling wine, which has necessitated both expansion and a big switch to new more suitable varieties.

One way it has financed its evolution and helped other growers without weighing itself down with debt has been to copy models common in both the New Zealand and Champagne wine industries. The produce of its own vineyards only supplies about 30 per cent of its needs, but Chapel Down now makes long-term supply contracts with other vineyards, many of them start-ups. It undertakes to buy its partners' harvests (subject to quality criteria), which gives them both the incentive and the confidence to invest in planting. Chapel Down shares with its partners the full benefit of its own expertise to ensure that good quality while spreading the risk of a poor harvest across several vineyards, therefore getting access to all the fruit it needs without having to commit to massive new investment and overhead.

In 2004 Chapel Down Group made the decision to float the company on the PLUS market. PLUS is an alternative to the London Stock Exchange for smaller companies looking to raise money by selling shares to investors. Current share prices for Chapel Down Group hover around £0.77. The funds raised from doing this allowed the company to upgrade its winery and increase production, particularly in the capital-heavy sparkling wine side of the business.

In January 2018, Chapel Down announced that it received valid applications to subscribe for £2.35m under the Open Offer. The Open Offer was to raise up to £1.47m and was heavily oversubscribed.

Tread carefully when buying fruit – some growers take umbrage at a sliding scale being offered based on ripeness, and don't necessarily understand that this is how grapes are sold the world over. Likewise, if you are the grower, realise that taking action in the vineyard to increase quality can result in higher prices, cancelling out any perceived loss of income from reduced yield. Also, achieving better-quality grapes year on year will give you a track record that will maintain a higher price even when your supply of grapes inevitably increases.

Winemaking costs

If you are making traditional method, bottle-fermented sparkling wine you will be making wine and squirrelling it away for nearly three years before you even attempt to sell any. Therefore, winemaking cost calculations need to take this delay in return into account.

The direct costs of making wine are the grapes, yeast and additions such as sugar, a bottle, a closure and the label. Other costs are overheads such as utilities, labour and capital expenditure on equipment. Just taking those direct costs can make winemaking an attractive proposition. However, the overheads can be huge and uncontrolled, and can far outweigh any potential return.

Still wine:
- £1,500 per tonne of grapes might yield 900 bottles, making the grape cost around £1.60 per bottle – growing your own grapes means you can hopefully reduce this figure.
- Yeast and other additions for the same 900 bottles might be £3 in total.
- Sugar to chaptalise/enrich by two per cent would cost around £20 or 2p per bottle.
- The bottle itself could be anything from 35p depending on weight, style and quality.
- A cork can vary in price from 15–25p, again depending on quality.

Case study
Attracting private investors – Hambledon Vineyard, Hampshire
www.hambledonvineyard.co.uk

Hambledon Vineyard in Hampshire might be called the birthplace of English winemaking. The first truly commercial vineyard and winery in England was planted by Major-General Sir Guy Salisbury-Jones in 1952, and past vintages of Hambledon wines have been served in British embassies around the world and in the Houses of Parliament.

Current owner Ian Kellett took over in 1999 and set about replanting with the holy trinity of sparkling wine grapes, Chardonnay, Pinot Noir and Pinot Meunier. Until the 2010 vintage, he sold the entire crop to other wine-producers across the country but in that year launched a campaign to raise £4 million through the tax-efficient Enterprise Investment Scheme. The minimum of £10,000 attracted well-off private investors with a taste for a flutter. The prospectus highlighted the speculative nature of the venture, but by spreading the risk over a wide pool of (fairly) small investors, the directors could reduce their own exposure in what is a notoriously fickle industry.

The success of the EIS also entitled Hambledon to a record grant of more than £500,000 from the South East England Development Agency, now defunct, and in 2011 the holding of 10 ha was extended by leasing 13 ha more and the winery was extended and re-equipped, producing its first vintage under the eagle eyes of consultant Hervé Jestin, previously Chef de Caves at Duval Leroy, and winemaker Antoine Arnault in 2013.

But it doesn't stop there. Kellett and his backers have invested some £10 million in transforming Hambledon over the last decade. At time of writing he is returning to the hunt for private investors, seeking another £4–5 million via crowdfunding to launch Hambledon towards a (distant) production target of a million bottles a year.

- A plain capsule will be less than 3p, while branded ones will be more.
- Label costs are also difficult to quantify and can vary hugely.
- The total cost will be at least £2.15 if you go for the cheapest of everything, and quite likely more.

This does not take into account the labour, the power required, interest on capital expenditure, interest paid on loans and boxes for final packaging.

Sparkling wine:
- Grapes for sparkling wine are more expensive and yield a lower volume of juice so £2,500 per tonne might only yield 800 bottles at a cost of around £3 per bottle.
- Yeast and other additions such as sugar for chaptalisation, would be similar to still wine.
- The bottles are heavier and therefore more expensive, starting at 50p per bottle for bulk orders and as much as 75p or more for smaller orders.
- Crown caps and bidules at tirage (bottling), along with more yeast and additions, would be 5–8p per bottle.
- Storage for a minimum nine months and more likely several years at a specialist facility would cost 20–30p per bottle.
- The cork and wire at disgorging would add another 30p.
- Foils, labels and boxes are all dependent on type and style.
- With more variables in terms of storage length, etc., sparkling wine could cost at least £4 per bottle before accounting for labour and power.

Getting the label right, as well as the foil and other packaging, can involve a branding agency, focus groups, graphic designers, marketing consultants, etc. – all before you even get to the type of paper and printer – and it can cost a fortune. There are specialist packaging suppliers such as Sparflex **www.sparflex.com** – a French company who have an office in the UK – who will do the whole design process (from a brief supplied by you) for a few thousand euros, as long as you get them to print and produce the labels.

Selling your wine

If you sell your wine direct to the consumer you will make the highest margin and the greatest gross profit – however, it might not be the most efficient way of selling. Taking on a distributor might seem unnecessary and reduce the margin that you can achieve, but once you are producing a significant volume, you may not be able to sell all your stock from the cellar door or manage the sales by yourself. It is easy to overlook the cost of your own time that might be better spent in the winery or vineyard, and how do you quantify the cost of the sales you have missed because you didn't have representation in the market?

Hiring a dedicated sales team or person is another option that probably isn't worth considering until you are producing hundreds of thousands of bottles. A good distributor will do all the legwork for you and has a sales team already working around the country. This is worth the reduced margin you will get by selling to them.

See Chapter Seven for more details on marketing.

Appendices

Appendix I

The following text is a summary of Notice 163 and is reproduced from HMRC website at **www.gov.uk/government/publications/excise-notice-163-wine-production**.

Notice 163 Wine Production (February 2018) – Summary

This notice replaces Notice 163 Wine Production (June 2017). It explains the regulations covering the production, storage and accounting for duty on wine and made-wine. The effects of the law and regulations covering the handling of wine in excise warehouses are explained in Notices 196 and 197. You will find the main legal provisions relating to the production, holding and movement of wine in the Alcoholic Liquor Duties Act 1979 and the Wine & Made-wine Regulations 1989.

Other legislation applying to wine producers includes the Customs & Excise Management Act 1979, the Revenue Traders (Accounts & Records) Regulations 1992, the Excise Goods (Holding, Movement & Duty Point) Regulations 2010, and the Excise Goods (Drawback) Regulations 1995. You can get copies of these from the Office of Public Sector Information. If you need help or advice, or any of the forms mentioned in this notice, contact the Excise Enquiries Helpline.

Wine and made wine

The Alcoholic Liquor Duties Act 1979 defines wine as liquor of a strength exceeding 1.2% ABV obtained from the fermentation of fresh grapes or the must of fresh grapes, whether or not it is fortified with spirits or flavoured with aromatic extracts.

Made-wine means liquor of a strength exceeding 1.2% similar to wine but not made from fresh grape. It includes RTDs made using fermented alcohol.

Sparkling wine is a wine carbonated to at least three bars and packaged in a bottle closed by mushroom cork and cage.

Excise-licensed premises – Applying for an excise licence

If you produce or sell wine, you must hold a wine producer's excise licence. To get an excise licence complete form WMW1 and either post or email it attaching your entry of premises. The postal address is: HM Revenue and Customs, Excise Processing Teams , BX9 1GL

If you have a question about your application once it has been sent, contact the Excise Processing Teams (EPT).

Your application will be subject to background checks. If these don't give enough assurance that the business is suitable for licensing, more information may be requested. Until this information is received, your application will be put on hold. A visit to your place of business may also be needed. It may take up to 45 days to process your application.

If we accept your application we will issue you with an excise licence which you should keep on the premises and produce to our officers on request. If we refuse we will give our reasons in writing and offer you a review of our decision or an appeal direct to the independent tribunal.

A separate licence is required for each premises at which you intend to make wine. However you may submit a single duty return for all your premises.

Your premises will be licensed as a tax warehouse but not as an excise warehouse. More information can be found in Notice 196 Excise goods: authorisation of warehouse keepers and Notice 197 Excise goods: receipt into and removal from an excise warehouse.

What your licence allows

As a licensed wine producer you can:
- produce wine on your premises
- store your wine on your premises in duty suspense
- receive wine from other authorised premises for further processing eg bottling in duty suspense

- receive back your own wine from other authorised premises after processing in duty suspense.

You may not receive spirits, beer, cider or imported wine in duty suspense or receive other producers' wine for sale. However commercial growers licensed as producers may receive wine made for them by another licensed producer.

To "make entry" of your premises you must prepare a plan showing the position and description of each vessel and other piece of plant you intend to use and where the wine will be stored. It should include any identifying marks on your vessels and plant and the full address of the premises. The plan should be submitted with your license application.

An on-site shop or bar is not considered part of the premises. Any wine stocked in the shop/bar must be duty-paid first.

Your licence will last until production ends. You must tell us in writing if you intend to stop production and when you have stopped production. After production has stopped and your wine is packaged you will have to pay duty due on any remaining stock and any unexplained shortages. We may also allow you to destroy the stock as if it were unfit for sale.

You can use your premises for other excise trades (for example, compounding spirits) provided you are licensed to carry out that trade and your working practices and records readily identify the trade being carried out in any room, vessel, or piece of equipment that can be used for two or more trades.

You must tell the EPT in writing about changes that may affect your licence. These include changes of ownership or legal identity and need a new application form WMW1 and entry of premises. You must also tell the EPT of changes of address, name of licensee or company, VAT status, the production of other excisable goods on the premises, and financial difficulties or impending insolvency. It may take up to 15 working days to make changes to your registration.

The production of wine for sale by a person who isn't licensed on premises which aren't licensed is an offence for which there is a penalty.

Duty

Duty is charged on the quantity and alcoholic strength (% ABV) of the wine calculated by reference to the package label or invoice. It is usually payable when wine is released from or consumed in excise-licensed premises or excise warehouses but may also be paid on the removal of wine held in duty suspense.

To calculate and pay the duty you must:

- keep records of all wine produced
- keep records of all wine leaving licensed premises, or otherwise passing the duty point
- calculate the duty due on all wine released for UK home market use
- keep records of all wine destroyed
- complete a monthly duty return and send it to the Central Collection Unit
- pay the duty by the due date by one of the methods described below.

You must also register for the Alcohol Wholesaler Registration Scheme if you sell duty-paid alcohol to another business. The purchaser is required to check that the wholesalers they buy from are enrolled with AWRS. To apply for approval, see Excise Notice 2002: Alcohol Wholesaler Registration Scheme.

We will ensure that duty is being correctly assessed and accounted for by auditing your commercial, accounting and management control systems and by physical checks on production, stock and movements of wine in duty suspension. When we want to carry out checks we will make an appointment. Occasionally we may visit without appointment, but the attending officer will give the reason for this. At any reasonable time you must allow our officers access to any area of the premises. You must make sure that all your security personnel are aware that we may visit without appointment. All our officers carry identification which they will show when they arrive.

If you fail to comply with the regulations relating to this notice or don't account for the correct amount of duty, we may take action including the issue of assessments and/or civil penalties. These are explained in Notice 208: Excise assessments and Notice 209: Civil Penalties: fixed, geared and daily.

Financial guarantees

Financial guarantees must be given by an approved guarantor (normally a bank or insurance company) to cover any shortfall and are the only form of security acceptable. To get a guarantee for intra-EU movements of wine or, if requested by us, for movements of wine within the UK, refer to section 10 of Notice 197 Excise goods: receipt into and removal from an excise warehouse of excise goods and then make a request in writing and send to:
HMRC , Financial Security Centre ,
Cotton House, 7 Cochrane Street,
Glasgow , G1 1GY.

   You won't have to provide a guarantee if you're eligible for authorisation under the Excise Payment Security System, which allows eligible businesses to defer payment of duty without a guarantee. To apply for EPSS you must have been VAT-registered for three years or more, although you can apply even if you traded below the VAT threshold but have been registered in an excise payment regime for three years or more. Your excise return, payment, and debt compliance history will be checked. To apply, complete form Excise Payment Security System: application to make payments of excise duties without a guarantee (EPSS(B)) and send it to:
EPSS Authorisation Team,
Ruby House, 8 Ruby Place,
Aberdeen, AB10 1ZP

   If you do require a guarantee, your guarantor must complete form Import and export: guarantee payment due using the Excise Payment Security System (C1201TAPS) and send it to:
HMRC Environmental Taxes Team,
Room ELG-03, St Mungo's Road,
Cumbernauld, Strathclyde, G70 5TR

   Your guarantee should be sufficient to cover all the duty likely to be due on wine removed from your premises to the UK home market in any given accounting period. If you fail to provide a guarantee, you must pay the duty due when it passes the duty point.

If you are not eligible for EPSS and you don't want to provide a guarantee you can pay a year's estimated duty liability in advance. Contact the Environmental Taxes Team to make the arrangements.

Duty rates and when duty becomes due

The duty rates for wine are structured in bands according to strength and whether it is sparkling or not. They are stated as amounts per hectolitre (100 litres). The Excise Enquiries Helpline will advise you of current rates of duty or you can find them in alcohol duty rates.

There are six categories for wine and made-wine:

- all wine/made-wine 1.2% ABV-4% ABV
- all wine/made-wine 4%-5.5% ABV
- still wine/made-wine 5.5%-15% ABV
- still wine/made-wine 15%-22% ABV
- sparkling wine 5.5%-8.5% ABV
- sparkling wine 8.5% ABV-15% ABV
- Any wines exceeding 22% ABV are dutied as spirits.

Wine is liable to the sparkling rates of duty if it is bottled with excess pressure due to CO_2 of three bars or more at 20°C and/or closed with a mushroom-shaped stopper held in place by a tie or fastening.

Duty only becomes payable when the wine leaves licensed premises unless it is being delivered to other approved premises for processing, to an excise warehouse, for export, for shipment as stores, to HM Ships, or to entitled diplomats or entitled members of visiting forces. Normally the duty should be paid by the 15th day after the end of your accounting period. If you think that it would help your business to pay duty before the wine leaves your premises, you may do so. This is called 'constructive removal'.

If you don't pay by the due date you will be liable to a civil penalty of 5% of the duty or £250, whichever is greater. More penalties may be incurred for each day that you fail to pay. Details are contained in

Excise Notice 209: civil penalties - fixed, geared and daily. At any time after the due date for payment, our officer may take action to take possession of wine, materials, and equipment and auction them to recover duty due and pay Taking Control of Goods fees.

Working out and paying duty

At the end of each accounting period agreed with HMRC total up all the wine sent out from your premises during that period, work out the duty, complete a duty account and transfer the appropriate totals to monthly return EX606 Wine/Made-Wine/Cider/Perry Return declaration. Round down the quantity of wine to the nearest litre.

Examples using duty rates in force at time of publication of this Notice:

- (a) 407 × 3-litre container of still wine at 11% ABV = 1,221 litres. 1,221 × duty rate of £2.7784 = £3,392.4264, rounded down to £3,392.42.
- (b) 137 cases of still wine, each containing 12 × 750ml bottles at 13% ABV. 12 × 750ml = 9 litres per case = 1,233 litres. 1,233 x £2.7784 = £3,425.7672, rounded down to £3,425.76.
- (c) 245 cases of sparkling wine, each containing 12 × 750ml at 12% ABV = 2,205 litres × £3.5587 = £7,846.9335 rounded down to £7,846.93.

Whenever the duty rate changes we will notify you of the new rates and the effective date and time of the change. Alternatively, find details of duty rate changes by contacting the Excise Enquiries Helpline. If the rate changes during an accounting period, you must complete separate returns for the period, one at the old rates and one at the new.

EX606s are routinely sent out to all licensed producers. If you don't receive one, contact the Environmental Taxes Team. Fill in your EX606 with the quantity of wine in each duty band you constructively removed) during the previous accounting period, any allowable deductions, and the amount of duty you owe.

If you don't send a return on time, you will be liable to penalties. We may estimate the duty due and pursue it through the civil courts. If you foresee problems, immediately contact the Environmental Taxes Team.

If you have more than one premises you may, on request, combine the duty liability for both on the same return. However an individual duty summary should be maintained for each site and consolidated in a duty account by the site submitting the return. If you are approved to produce both cider and wine/made-wine you may, as above, combine the duty liability for both products and /or premises.

If you make no deliveries of wine during an accounting period, you must still send us an EX606. Insert 'nil' in the quantities box, sign the return and send to us.

If you submit a false or inaccurate return you may be liable to a penalty. If you are aware you have made a mistake on your return, you must tell us as soon as possible. Depending on circumstances we may reduce the penalty. If you deliberately make a false duty return, you may face prosecution for the offence and incur a heavy penalty. You have the right to appeal against a penalty.

Send returns to:

HMRC, Central Collection Unit (TAPS), Alexander House, 21 Victoria Avenue, Southend-on-Sea, S99 1AS

Measurement of quantity and alcoholic strength

Quantity

We can ask for duty to be accounted for on the actual quantity of wine in each container as it passes the duty point. However, most packagers use the 'average system' of quantity control. Within specified limits, the actual contents of any particular container may be more or less than the declared contents, but the system conforms to a Weights & Measures Code of Practice which has been agreed with Trading Standards. Packagers are obliged to monitor and record the actual quantity of wine by sampling a proportion of packages to make sure they fulfil the code's requirement.

When removing small-pack wine (ie containers of 10 litres or less)

for UK consumption, you should charge duty on the quantity declared on the label. Evidence of compliance with weights and measures legislation will be sufficient to accept the labelled contents as the duty base unless there are grounds for believing that deliberate duty avoidance is involved.

You must take at least one sample (minimum of five packages) from each production run. The average of the samples taken to comply with average contents rules will be treated as the quantity of wine in a container. You must monitor the filling process to make sure that the quantity packaged does not regularly excessively exceed the amount declared on the label. Record these checks and provide an adequate audit trail to establish due diligence. Where there is evidence of consistent and excessive overfilling, more duty will be due. If you cannot produce accurate records upon which the extra duty can be readily established, we will use best judgement.

Containers of 10 litres or more should be dipped, metered or weighed to ascertain their actual dutiable content.

Alcohol

Alcoholic strength is assessed as the percentage ABV in the wine at 20°C truncated to one decimal place so that 5.59% ABV becomes 5.5% ABV. You may use any method to measure it that produces results that agree with the distillation analysis or reference method. If you don't use distillation analysis to measure your ABV, you must be prepared to explain your method and show that your results agree with it. For any methods not based on laboratory analysis an independent analyst must test the ABV of each of your products at least annually. The results must be held in your business records.

For duty purposes, the alcoholic strength of wine is the actual strength when it passes the duty point. However if you comply with certain conditions we will accept the declared strength. To use the declared strength, you must be able to show that you have used due diligence in the control of your process to make sure that, on average, the actual ABV of each finished product equates to what you are declaring. This requires continuous monitoring and recording of your

ABV results. It is understood that the ABV of the same product may occasionally vary, but provided appropriate action is taken quickly to return the strength of the wine to within its normal specification, due diligence will have been demonstrated. You must keep records of action taken to maintain product strength within control limits.

We may take samples of wine which will be analysed using the reference method . The analysis result will establish the actual dutiable strength of the wine for legal purposes.

Duty reliefs

Natural losses, wastage and other legitimate causes for lost product are not liable to duty if we're satisfied that they are genuine. There is therefore provision for duty relief on:

- accidental losses on licensed production premises
- spoilt wine or wine otherwise unfit for use
- trade samples
- wine for your own domestic consumption

Normally there is no duty relief in for wine which is lost after it has passed the duty point.

As a licensed wine producer, you're responsible for the control of wine in your premises. You must have the necessary systems to control and safeguard your stocks. You must examine critically all losses and deficiencies. Your records of production and processing should show how much wine you lose during routine operations: for example, the losses you incur during packaging.

For accidental losses you must record:

- the date and time the loss occurred
- the product name and the volume lost, and the alcoholic strength if the loss occurred after production had been completed
- the vessels in which it was contained, and
- the reason why the loss occurred

If wine can't be accounted for after the start of production, and there is no acceptable explanation, you are liable for duty on the missing wine. It is in your own interest to keep proper records of all losses.

You won't have to pay the duty if we're satisfied the wine has been unintentionally spoilt, contaminated or otherwise rendered unfit for consumption and hasn't been consumed. You can write of' the quantities after you have recorded the information and destroyed any spoilt product. But we may examine your records, and if we're not satisfied with your explanation and supporting evidence you will have to pay the duty on the quantity previously written off. You must record the same information for spoiled wine as for accidental losses (above).

Destroying duty suspended wine without paying duty

If duty suspended wine is damaged or in a non-marketable condition, you can destroy it without paying the duty as long as you follow the correct procedures.

You must give us at least five working days' notice with details of the proposed method of destruction and satisfy us that your proposed process will destroy the intrinsic nature of the wine. Write to or email the Customs International Trade and Excise (CITEX) Written Enquiry Team and give the following details:

*   why you wish to destroy the goods
*   details of the goods
*   the amount of duty involved
*   where and when the proposed destruction will take place
*   the method of destruction

If the wine is to be removed from licensed premises to be destroyed at a specialist destruction site there must be a complete audit trail which confirms the wine has been destroyed under the supervision of either an Authorised Company Representative (ACR) of the wine producer, or a person within the specialist destruction company who has been appointed by the producer to supervise the destruction on their behalf. This person must be at management or supervisory level. A Certificate must be obtained from the company as evidence of destruction.

Products for reprocessing

You may re-ferment any wine or residues which are taken from duty-unpaid stocks on your licensed premises. Enter the quantity of wine in your production records. Make sure your records are accurately and promptly updated so we can verify the quantities. You may also be eligible to claim a refund of duty paid on wine which has been returned to your licensed premises for reprocessing .

Reprocessing includes the following operations:

- the mixing of one wine with another (or others) on licensed premises
- the filtering or repasteurising of wine.

Spoilt wine

You don't have to pay duty on wine which is accidentally lost or spoilt on your premises. If wine becomes spoilt or otherwise unfit for use after leaving your premises you can claim a refund on any wine returned to you provided it was produced by you and has not undergone any further process or dilution since leaving your premises. Adulterated wine containing additions which we have not approved, wine for which no satisfactory audit trail is available, and wine spoiled more than three years after the duty was paid are not eligible for relief.

You don't have to destroy spoilt wine to claim duty relief; it can also be reprocessed. However you may destroy spoilt wine at any time subject to any notice of destruction that may be required (see below), but entitlement to reclaim the duty on spoilt wine depend on these conditions:

- a full audit trail must be maintained
- the requirements of other regulatory authorities such as the Environment Agency must be observed
- proper control practices are maintained, including appropriate action at management and supervisory levels

To reclaim duty on wine destroyed away from your premises there must be a complete audit trail which confirms the wine has been destroyed and that it was duty paid, and the destruction must be supervised by an Authorised Company Representative appointed by the producer, named in their records and trained in their requirements. Destructions at specialist sites may be supervised by a person of supervisory or management level within the destruction company. A certificate must be obtained from the company as evidence of destruction.

Spoilt wine relief also requires evidence of a full credit of the duty paid value, or replacement of the goods to your customer (or owner of the goods at the time they became spoilt).

HMRC will advise you if you need to give notice; otherwise you can destroy the wine when you want. If notice is required, you must give at least: two working days' notice if you want to destroy wine on your premises or five working days' notice if you want to destroy wine outside your premises

You must give details of the proposed method of destruction and destroy the wine in a way that makes it unsaleable as a beverage.

To make a claim, total the entries in your spoilt wine record of all wine destroyed or reprocessed during the accounting period and transfer the total to your wine duty account. When you submit your next monthly return, deduct the duty you are reclaiming by entering it against lines 23 to 32 on the reverse of the EX606 as appropriate and carry the total to line 36.

When auditing claims, we examine your business records and supporting evidence. If we are not satisfied with your explanation and evidence, you will have to repay the duty you claimed.

When wine is either returned for destruction or destroyed remotely, you must enter the following particulars in the destruction section of your spoilt wine record:
- the total volume of spoilt wine destroyed
- the strength of the spoilt wine destroyed
- the date and time of the destruction
- the place and method of destruction
- the volume and strength of the wine in each container from which the spoilt wine was directly destroyed
- evidence of the amount of duty charged or paid
- the amount of spoilt wine relief claimed

- the description of the wine returned by each purchaser in respect of which a claim is made
- the name and address of each purchaser, and
- the numbers and sizes of each container in which the wine was returned by each purchaser returning the wine.

When wine is returned for reprocessing, the same particulars must be entered in the
reprocessing section of your spoilt wine record. Unless we allow a longer period, your spoilt wine record must be completed within one hour of reprocessing taking place.

Samples
You may take production and reference samples for analysis and organoleptic appreciation (but not consumption) in your premises as long as you enter the quantities and reasons for removal in your samples records. These samples should be used up in tests, destroyed or returned to process when you have finished with them. You may also take genuine trade samples as long as you enter the quantities and reasons for removal in your samples records. Trade samples must:

- not be intended for consumption
- be restricted to quantities not exceeding one litre per product
- be clearly labelled 'NOT FOR SALE'
- be supplied only to a wholesaler or distributor or to a potential trade customer within the UK

If they are not supplied free of charge then you must pay duty on them.

Wine used for promotions and for tasting at, for example, trade fairs, shows, exhibitions and supermarkets must be duty-paid. You may take duty-paid samples for any business purpose. There is no restriction on size or number.

Wine that you or your employees drink
If you are a grower or beekeeper who produces, or has produced

for you, wine from your own fruit or honey, you can have approved quantities of wine for your own consumption, or for drinking free of charge by your employees, free of duty.

The term 'grower' refers to the owners or lessees of vines for whose cultivation, nurturing and harvesting they are responsible. Growers may contract others to carry out the work for them, but they are responsible for its supervision.

Entitlement to relief is based on the quantity of wine produced in the preceding calendar year and cannot be carried forward from one year to the next. The maximum quantity which can be used for domestic drinking free of duty in any calendar year is 5.5 hectolitres plus 10% of the quantity above 5.5 hectolitres produced in the preceding calendar year. However the total must not be more than 11 hectolitres. To claim this relief, record your domestic consumption in your business records before you remove your entitlement.

Wine supplied by the glass free of any charge including admission to guests may be taken from your domestic consumption allowance.

Vine leasing for domestic consumption

Lessees of vines can receive wine duty-free if it is for their own domestic use. You may be asked by our officer to produce contracts or agreements for inspection. Lessee may only receive wine produced from their own grapes. They must take responsibility for all the work on their vines such as the cultivation, nurturing, harvesting and present the grapes from their own vines for vinification by a winemaker. They may contract others to carry out the work for them, but are responsible for supervising contracted work. Vineyard owners may not attend to the cultivation, nurturing or harvesting of leased vines unless they or their employees are separately contracted to do so by the lessee. They may not supplement the harvest of any leased vines from any other source or allow lessees to take their grapes elsewhere for vinification, and must maintain records of each lessee and the quantity of grapes presented for vinification with dates and times

Vineyard owners may vinify the grapes from more than one lessee at the same time, but each lessee must receive only that proportion of wine which relates to their grapes. If any of these rules are not observed, the wine produced will be liable to duty.

Documents required for movements within the UK

All intra-UK movements of wine will be submitted through the Excise Movement & Control System (EMCS) unless they qualify for the simplified procedures. An electronic administrative document (eAD) will have to be raised on EMCS before the movement can start. EMCS automatically allocates an Administrative Reference Code (ARC) that uniquely identifies the movement. The ARC will be on the printed copy of the eAD or should be noted on the commercial document and must travel with the goods.

If movements of wine are under simplified procedures your normal commercial despatch documents will be suitable if they have:

- the name and address of your premises
- a unique reference number
- the name and address of the premises you are sending the wine to
- the date of despatch
- a description of the wine, including the quantity
- a statement indicating that the wine is being moved in duty suspension

Records and Accounts

As a revenue trader, you must observe the requirements of Excise Notice 206: revenue traders' records. We need you to maintain and produce for examination a record of your business activities. We may examine:

- profit and loss and trading statements
- management accounts and reports
- balance sheets and trading forecasts
- internal and external auditor's reports
- any record maintained for a business purpose

Under regulation 6 of the Revenue Trader (Accounts & Records)

Regulations 1992 you must keep records which show:

- materials used (including additives)
- details of processes and operations including fermentations, additions, drawing off, bottling & packaging
- quantities and strength of wine produced, received, sent out from or returned to premises, constructively removed, lost or destroyed on premises, rendered sparkling
- samples
- domestic consumption
- imports
- exports
- receipts
- details of stock-takes, including details of any surplus, deficiency or other discrepancy revealed by the stock-take

You must also keep a duty account conforming to 5(1) of the Revenue Trader (Accounts & Records) Regulations 1992 containing:

- the amount of duty on all wine that leaves duty suspension
- the amount of duty reclaimed on spoilt wine which has been destroyed or wine which has been reprocessed
- the amount of any underdeclarations or overdeclarations from previous periods, and
- the net amount of duty due for the period and the date and method of payment

You must keep your business records for six years or get our agreement before destroying any of your records that are less than six years old. You can keep them on any form of storage technology as long as copies can be easily produced and there are adequate facilities for allowing our officer to view them when required. You should advise the Excise Enquiries Helpline before you transfer records. You may need to operate the old and new systems side by side for a period. Ensure that you keep your original registration certificate in a safe place.

Appendix II
Planning permission

Throughout the text we have touched on planning issues as they have arisen. But even though growing grapes is an agricultural activity and agriculture enjoys a more relaxed planning regime than any other area of the UK's economic life, planning impinges on the winegrower's life at so many different points that perhaps it is worth a more detailed review.

First things first: are you actually buying a farm? Viticulture is an agricultural use and all the land on which you carry it out must therefore be agricultural land. Make sure – or rather, make sure your solicitor makes sure – that all the acreage that comprises your purchase is registered for agricultural use. As a general rule it's possible to farm pretty much any plot of land on a commercial or at least semi-commercial basis without having to obtain planning permission. You can sell bedding plants and surplus fruit and veg from your garden without anybody's permission, which many people do; and although the sale of produce from allotments is often forbidden, that would be a condition of the lease rather than a planning matter. But if your large suburban garden were suddenly to vanish beneath the vines à la Tom and Barbara Good, that would be a very different matter; and if part of the land you've just bought has recreational use – as a riding school, say – then you do require change of use permission before ploughing up the paddock and planting a few rows of vines instead. Of course it would go through on the nod: sensible planning officers would probably approve it themselves under Delegated Powers without even putting the application to the Development Control Committee.

But that doesn't mean that there's no regulation at all: some of your purchase might be woodland, for instance, in which case you'll need a felling licence from the Forestry Commission before clearing it (and this may be tricky as the Commission's brief is to encourage landowners to plant more trees rather than uproot the trees they've already got), and the local council might very well take a more than passing interest and insist on a formal application being made for change of use. And unless there's established agricultural use, planning officers will want to have oversight of matters such as noise, nuisance, access, and traffic generation.

Your solicitor might very well not look out for hurdles of this kind simply because they're not run-of-the-mill; a nudge from you before contracts are exchanged might save a lot of bother later on.

Permitted development

Once you are satisfied that the land you now possess is indeed agricultural, things become a great deal easier thanks to the magic of Permitted Development. PD is the obvious and sensible provision included in successive Town & Country Planning Acts and all their various associated Orders that, to make any sense, if one permitted activity necessitates another then the second should be permitted too. A chicken shed requires a feed silo. An arable farm requires a grain-dryer, a granary, and a tractor shed. And although a vineyard doesn't absolutely require a winery – indeed, nearly four-fifths of vineyards don't have one – winemaking is clearly ancillary to grape-growing and if you are a grower, and crucially, provided your land is an established agricultural unit, then a winery is a PD and doesn't need planning permission.

The legal basis for all this is actually rather flimsy and goes back to the 1999 Appeal Court case of Millington vs the Department of the Environment and Shrewsbury & Atcham Borough Council. It was a complicated case in which, following complaints from the public, the council issued an Enforcement Notice to prevent David Millington of Wroxeter Roman Vineyard from holding tastings and selling wine in his winery and from giving guided tours of his vineyard. Both activities were understandably popular and attracted a volume of visitors that the locals and the council felt (with some justification) that the narrow lanes connecting Wroxeter to the outside world couldn't sustain. Without going into too much detail Mr Millington appealed, the appeals inspector backed him, the DoE overturned its own inspector's decision and the Appeal Court overturned the DoE's overturning of... well. Somewhere along the way the DoE interpolated a completely spurious ruling that a winery wasn't ancillary to a vineyard (a point that had never been part of the original case) but unilaterally granted Mr Millington planning permission for the winery he already had. This the three Appeal Judges rejected unanimously; and the upshot, although never spelt out in so many words, was that a winery is ancillary and therefore a PD that needs no planning permission, but shops and tours aren't and do. It's not set in stone, but it's a convention that both the industry and local authorities seem to be able to live with.

PD status, although it seems to have been safely established for wineries, doesn't give you carte blanche to build a massive factory in beautiful farmland. There are many restrictions that you have to observe. One is size: 465 square metres is the maximum permitted. A second is that you can only use it to process your own fruit – so, no contract winemaking. A third is that you can't live in it! It mustn't be within 25 metres of a classified road. It has to be on agricultural land – you can't build the winery in the garden of your house and claim it's a permitted development. PD doesn't apply in Areas of Outstanding Natural Beauty or National Parks either. But it does apply to the conversion of existing buildings – from a granary to a winery, say – provided the original building is under 465 square metres, the conversion doesn't increase its height, and the extension doesn't increase its cubic capacity.

Historic properties

If you propose to site your winery in a historic property of some sort – an ancient barn, say, or one of the outbuildings of a great country house - then you may or may not need change of use permission: the old barn, being on agricultural land, will have PD status; a converted stable probably won't because a stableyard isn't agricultural land. In both cases you will almost certainly need a separate permission as well, and one that can be quite hard to get.

Buildings of this kind are usually protected by statutory listing (check **www.britishlistedbuildings.co.uk**) to confirm whether you chosen building is listed or not) and require listed building consent before you can make any alterations or even repairs that affect their character or appearance, however insignificantly. There are also restrictions, albeit far fewer, to what changes you can make to buildings in Conservation Areas. Strictly speaking, this is not part of your change of use application as it's covered by different laws; but in practice the two applications can be submitted at the same time. They remain separate applications, though, and the outcome of one doesn't affect the outcome of the other. You can be granted listed building consent on the grounds that your proposals don't affect the building's character, but still be refused change of use permission on the grounds that vehicle access is inadequate. Refusal of either application can be challenged; so if you're knocked back on the one but get through on the other, the game's not up.

Shops and visitor centres

We are way beyond PD and Delegated Powers territory when it comes to taking the next step and welcoming tourists and shoppers through your gates. We are now in the territory of full-blown planning applications and the message is – don't be afraid! Planning officers don't bite!

Actually, getting planning permission really is more straightforward these days than it used to be; and thanks to the web, it's also much easier to get the information you need than it used to be. At **www.planningportal.gov.uk** you'll find a pretty exhaustive guide to planning matters; it even enables you to apply online and includes a fee calculator to help you work out roughly how much the council will charge you. It also has links to other sites detailing, for instance, national policy on converting surplus agricultural buildings to other employment-related uses. (Comfortingly, Public Planning Guidance note 7 makes a presumption that councils should approve 'well-conceived farm diversification proposals, particularly involving the re-use of existing buildings for business purposes'). Another useful link is to the Royal Town Planning Institute's site **www.rtpi.org.uk**, which includes a list of planning and development consultants. Hopefully you won't need one, but if your application is any less than perfectly straightforward, you very well might.

Local Development Framework

Your first port of call, when planning the new builds necessary to expand and diversify the business activities carried out on your vineyard and/or winery site, should be the Local Development Framework, the modern successor to the old District Plan, which sets out the council's general planning policies and specifies permissible land uses locality by locality throughout its territory. Checking the LDF should really be part of the purchasing process, to give you a good idea even before you buy your existing vineyard or virgin plot what its future is likely to be. When perusing the LDF either at the town or city hall or on the council's website, be sure to check carefully whether permissions for a shop (use class A1) or a cafe/restaurant (use class A3) likely to be granted for your site, or does the LDF frown on the volume of traffic they are likely to generate? (When you eventually come to build your distillery, planning should not be a big issue. Distilling is B2, light industrial not suitable in a residential area; and because raw materials are made on-site and the goods going off-site are high value but small volume it won't generate an appreciable number of traffic movements).

Consultation

Modern planning is, to a large extent, about transparency and consultation. Planning has always been about measuring the impact of proposed developments on the surrounding area, but in the patriarchal past, the public was much less involved. Members of the public could object, but their opinions weren't actively canvassed and they weren't allowed to speak at council meetings. Fire, police, and highways authorities were consulted, but in private at the golf club or Masonic Lodge rather than by way of publicly available documents.

Planning regulations stipulate who should be consulted and how, and the best way to start the process is to make friends with the people in Development Control and then do exactly what they tell you, preferably with a willing smile. There's no guarantee that problems won't arise; but opening a good channel of communications with the planning officer working on your proposal is the best way of avoiding the risk. You will have to pay an administration fee to cover the costs of your application anyway, but some councils will charge extra for an initial consultation with your planning officer. However, as it's this very officer who will recommend acceptance or rejection of your plan to the Development Control Committee, the extra charge is money well spent. Involving this officer in the evolution of your visitor centre and shop makes it almost as much his or her baby as yours. So by the time the application is ready to be formally considered, the two of you should have made it almost watertight. Of course, this process may itself have ups and downs, but remember, if your planning officer flatly vetoes an idea of yours, it's not out of bloody-mindedness but out of an intimate knowledge of local policies and a very shrewd understanding of what will or won't be approved.

As we've said, the planning officer's main concern after the design and suitability of the application building itself will be its local impact, especially if there are any residents in the immediate area. This concern is partly met by the LDF's approved uses for the locality. But as far as the building itself is concerned, there's quite a long list of boxes to tick. Can it jump all the relevant health and safety hoops? How good is the vehicle access? Is there room on the site for all employees, visitors and deliveries to park off-street and for vehicles to manoeuvre, i.e. for articulated lorries to reverse? Is the premises in a conservation area, an Area of Outstanding Natural Beauty, or a National Park? Is the design suitable for the locality? How many traffic movements on and off site do you envisage? Can you control noise and emissions to the satisfaction of local residents, if there are any? Other necessary compliances involve building regulations, health and safety matters, and waste water disposal, and you may find that the council won't give you the final go-ahead unless these compliances, especially the last two, are fully dealt with in your application.

Consultation starts with advertisements both in the local press (another expense!) and on the application premises to give residents the chance to object if they fear your plans will affect the amenity of the area. But the grounds on which they can object are limited by statute, and the planning authority is specifically instructed (see the Planning Portals website again) that the mere number of objections is irrelevant. Petitions are a waste of time and effort in plannin. The presumption is that you are free to do whatever you want on your property provided there are no valid reasons why you shouldn't; 100 people saying they just don't want you to isn't valid, because it's your property. But it only takes a single person pointing out that local drains can't take the amount of effluent you'll be creating to put the kybosh on the whole thing.

Your main consultations, though, will be with other statutory bodies: the local council's own environmental health department; the county council as highways authority; the parish council; the Environment Agency; and the Health & Safety Executive. This is the part of the process that really takes the time, and it's these agencies that are likeliest to have objections. Be prepared to alter your blueprints to satisfy their observations, always in consultation with your friendly planning officer; work with rather than against all these people and by the time you have finished your application it should be virtually watertight and go through on the nod.

In law, councils have to determine your application within eight weeks of receiving it, but they have the power to extend the permitted period under certain circumstances. If they do, you can appeal to the Secretary of State, but it's rather self-defeating as the appeal will take longer than the council would. So if you want your application to be determined as quickly as possible – and if you want to be sure of getting the right result – then everything hinges on thorough preparation and good communication. What this means, in effect, is that the whole planning process will take longer – a lot longer – than eight weeks – eight months, more like! But the bulk of the work will be done before your application actually goes in.

Appeals
The important thing is not to be afraid and some people are. They

think the council is there to frustrate them, or tie them up in red tape, and the only sure way to get an application through is to sneak it under the town hall's radar somehow. And while it's true that councils can be awkward if they want to be, and that there are more formalities to go through than there are at the State Opening of Parliament, in essence the council is there to help you and has an obligation to make suitable provision for developments such as yours. The grounds on which applications can be refused or substantially varied are finite; and if you discover in advance what they are, you shouldn't find it hard to put together an application that is more or less bound to succeed.

But what if you fall at this stage? The obvious thing is to appeal, and you have six months from the rejection of your application to do so. Once again, the Planning Portal contains all the details you need – you can even appeal online! Appeals are handled by the Planning Inspectorate, which appoints an independent inspector to whom you can both state your own case and comment on the planning authority's statement of case. The inspectorate also appoints a case officer who will help you by telling you what documentation to present and when, although you may need the advice of an experienced surveyor or planning consultant.

An appeal is the only way to overcome refusal of listed building consent; but if you are refused change of use permission, a quicker and cheaper option is to find out what the council didn't like about your application, amend it accordingly, and resubmit it. If you do this within 12 months there will be no fee; and objections to the original application are considered to have been dealt with already and can't be submitted again. This is the way large corporations wear down local objectors – they simply present slightly altered applications again and again until their opponents either run out of new objections or are simply too worn down to continue. That's perhaps not quite what you have in mind; but if you have been refused on minor or technical grounds this is the simplest solution.

Once you have been granted planning permission, you have three years to act on it before it expires.

Directory of services and suppliers

This directory is reproduced by kind permission of WineGB.

Vineyard – Consultants

Agrovista UK Ltd
Contact: Alex Radu
Rutherford House, Nottingham Science
& Technology Park, University Boulevard,
Nottingham, NG7 2PZ
Tel: +44 (0)115 939 0202
www.agrovista.co.uk

English Terroir Ltd
Contact: Owen Elias
Spots Farm Cottage, Small Hythe,
Tenterden, Kent, TN30 7NG
Tel: +44 (0)1580 763646
www.englishterroir.com

FAST LLP
Crop Technology Centre, Brogdale Farm
Brogdale Road,
Faversham, Kent, ME13 8XZ
Tel: +44 (0)1795 533225
www.fastllp.com

Halfpenny Green Vineyards
Contact: Clive Vickers
Tom Lane, Bobbington,
South Staffs, DY7 5EP
Tel: +44 (0)1384 221122

Haygrove Evolution Ltd
Contact: Simon Day, Production Director
Redbank, Ledbury, Herefordshire, HR8 2JL
Tel: +44 (0)1531 637119
www.haygrove-evolution.com

Hutchinsons (Main Office)
Contact: Chris Cooper
Weasenham Lane, Wisbech,
Cambridgeshire, PE13 2RN
Tel: +44 (0)1945 461177
www.hlhltd.co.uk

McNeill Vineyard Management Ltd
Contact: Duncal McNeil
Blagdon, Peartree Lane, Bicknacre,
Essex, CM3 4LS
Tel +44 (0)7972 668370
www.wvm.uk.com

Plumpton College
Contact: Chris Foss
Ditchling Road, Lewes,
East Sussex, BN7 3AE
Tel: +44 (0)1273 890454
www.plumpton.ac.uk

Sedlescombe Organic Vineyard
Contact: Roy Cook
Hawkhurst Road, Cripps Corner,
Robertsbridge East Sussex, TN32 5SA
Tel: +44 (0)1580 830715
www.englishorganicwine.co.uk

Stephen Skelton MW
1B Lettice Street, London, SW6 4EH
Tel: +44 (0)7768 583700
www.englishwine.com

Three Choirs Vineyards Ltd
Contact: Kevin Shayle
Newent, Gloucestershire, GL18 1LS
Tel: +44 (0)1531 890555
www.three-choirs-vineyards.co.uk

Veni Vidi Viti Ltd
Contact: Jim Newsome
1 Lloyts Croft Cottages, Church Road
Partridge Green, West Sussex,
RH13 8JR
www.veni-vidi-viti.com

Vine Care UK Ltd
Contact: Paul Woodrow-Hill
11 Penfolds Place, Arundel,
West Sussex BN18 9SA
Tel: +44 (0)1243 210241
www.vinecareuk.com

Vine Works Ltd
Contact: D'Arcy Gander
Unit 20, St Helena Farm, St Helena Lane
Plumpton Green,
East Sussex, BN7 3DH
Tel: +44 (0)1273 891777
www.vine-works.com

Vineyard Solutions
Contact: Ian Phillips
Baddow Park, West Hanningfield, Great
Baddow Chelmsford, Essex, CM2 7SY
Tel: +44 (0)1245 476994
www.vineyardsolutions.co.uk

Contract – Winemaking

Bolney Wine Estate
Contact: Liz Garrett
Foxhole Lane, Bolney,
West Sussex, RH17 5NB
Tel: +44 (0)1444 881575
www.bolneywineestate.com

Campden BRI (Wines & Spirits)
Contact: Geoff Taylor
Centenary Hall, Coopers Hill Road, Nutfield
Surrey, RH1 4HY
Tel: +44 (0)1737 822272
www.campdenbri.co.uk

English Terroir Ltd
Contact: Owen Elias
Spots Farm Cottage, Small Hythe,
Tenterden Kent, TN30 7NG
Tel: +44 (0)1580 763646
www.englishterroir.com

Halfpenny Green Vineyards
Contact: Clive Vickers
Tom Lane, Bobbington,
South Staffs, DY7 5EP
Tel: +44 (0)1384 221122
www.halfpenny-green-vineyards.co.uk

Hattingley Valley Wines Ltd
Wield Yard, Lower Wield, Alresford
Hampshire, SO24 9AJ
Tel: +44 (0)1256 389188
www.hattingleyvalley.co.uk

Haygrove Evolution Ltd
Contact: Simon Day, Production Director
Redbank, Ledbury,
Herefordshire, HR8 2JL
Tel: +44 (0)1531 637119
www.haygrove-evolution.com

Litmus Wines Ltd
London Road, Dorking, Surrey, RH5 6AA
Tel: +44 (0)1306 879829
www.litmuswines.com

Ridgeview Wine Estate
Contact: Robin Langton, COO
Ridgeview Wine Estate, Fragbarrow Lane
Ditchling Common,
Sussex, BN6 8TP
Tel: +44 (0)1444 242040
www.ridgeview.co.uk

Sedlescombe Organic Vineyard
Hawkhurst Road, Cripps Corner,
Robertsbridge East Sussex, TN32 5SA
Tel: +44 (0)1580 830715
www.englishorganicwine.co.uk

Stanlake Park Wine Estate
Contact: Vince Gower
The Winery, Stanlake Park, Twyford
Berkshire, RG10 0BN
Tel: +44 (0)118 9340176
www.stanlakepark.com

Three Choirs Vineyards Ltd
Contact: Kevin Shayle
Newent, Gloucestershire, GL18 1LS
Tel: +44 (0)1531 890555
www.three-choirs-vineyards.co.uk

Wiston Estate Winery
Contact: Dermot Sugrue
North Farm, London Road, Washington
West Sussex, RH20 4BB
Tel: +44 (0)1903 877845
www.wistonestate.com

Contract - Vineyard

Growth Industries
Contact: Russell Walker
Marche House, Woodland Drive,
Hove, BN3 7RA
Tel: +44 (0)7785 763678

Three Choirs Vineyards Ltd
Contact: Kevin Shayle
Newent, Gloucestershire, GL18 1LS
Tel: +44(0)1531 890555
www.three-choirs-vineyards.co.uk

Vine Care UK Ltd
Contact: Paul Woodrow-Hill
11 Penfolds Place, Arundel,
West Sussex BN18 9SA
Mobile: +44 (0) 7811 613141
www.vinecareuk.com

Vine Works Ltd
Contact: D'Arcy Gander
Unit 20, St Helena Farm, St Helena Lane

Plumpton Green,
East Sussex, BN7 3DH
Tel: +44 (0) 1273 891777
www.vine-works.com

Vineyard Dynamics
Contact: Andrew Sacha
77 Pullman Lane, Godalming,
Surrey, GU7 1YB
Tel: +44 (0)7931 365762
www.vineyarddynamics.com

Vineyard Solutions
Contact: Ian Phillips
Baddow Park, West Hanningfield,
Great Baddow, Chelmsford, Essex, CM2 7SY
Tel: +44 (0)1245 476994
www.vineyardsolutions.co.uk

Consultants - Winemaking

Bevtech Ltd
Contact: David Cowderoy
Moonhill Farm, Burgess Hill Road, Ansty
Haywards Heath, RH17 5AH
Tel: +44(0)1444 411141
www.bevtech.co.uk

English Terroir Ltd
Contact: Owen Elias
Spots Farm Cottage, Small Hythe,
Tenterden, Kent, TN30 7NG
Tel: +44 (0)1580 763646
www.englishterroir.com

Hattingley Valley Wines Ltd
Wield Yard, Lower Wield, Alresford,
Hampshire, SO24 9AJ
Tel: +44 (0)1256 389188
www.hattingleyvalley.co.uk

Haygrove Evolution Ltd
Contact: Simon Day, Production Director
Redbank, Ledbury,

Herefordshire, HR8 2JL
Tel: +44 (0)1531 637119
www.haygrove-evolution.com

Litmus Wines Ltd
London Road, Dorking, Surrey, RH5 6AA
Tel: +44 (0)1306 879829
www.litmuswines.com

Plumpton College
Contact: Chris Foss
Ditchling Road, Lewes,
East Sussex, BN7 3AE
Tel: +44 (0)1273 890454
www.plumpton.ac.uk

Stephen Skelton MW
1B Lettice Street, London, SW6 4EH
Tel: +44 (0)7768 583700
Email: spskelton@btinternet.com
www.englishwine.com

Three Choirs Vineyards Ltd
Contact: Kevin Shayle
Newent, Gloucestershire, GL18 1LS
Tel: +44(0)1531 890555 (option 1)
www.three-choirs-vineyards.co.uk

UK Wine Services Ltd
Contact: Ben Walgate
3 Garden Close, Woodchurch,
Kent, TN26 3NX
www.ukwineservices.org

Suppliers of grapevines

English Terroir Ltd
Contact: Owen Elias
Spots Farm Cottage, Small Hythe,
Tenterden Kent, TN30 7NG
Tel: +44(0)1580 763646
www.englishterroir.com

Haygrove Evolution Ltd
Contact: Simon Day, Production Director
Redbank, Ledbury, Herefordshire, HR8 2JL
Tel: +44(0)1531 637119
www.haygrove-evolution.com

Pépinières Tourette
Contact: Pierre-Denis Tourette
2210 Route d'Aubenas,
07 200 Vogüé, France
Tel: +33 475 377103
www.pepinieres-tourette.fr

Sedlescombe Organic Vineyard
Contact: Roy Cook
Hawkhurst Road, Cripps Corner,
Robertsbridge East Sussex, TN32 5SA
Tel: +44(0)1580 830715
www.englishorganicwine.co.uk

Three Choirs Vineyards Ltd
Contact: Kevin Shayle
Newent, Gloucestershire, GL18 1LS
Tel: +44(0)1531 890555
www.three-choirs-vineyards.co.uk

Vine Care UK Ltd
Contact: Paul Woodrow-Hill
11 Penfolds Place, Arundel,
West Sussex BN18 9SA
ww.vinecareuk.com

The Vine House (UK) Ltd
Contact: Jon Fletcher
Orchard Cottage, Leppington Lane,
Leppington Malton, YO17 9RL
Tel: +44(0)1653 658035
www.thevinehouse.co.uk

Vine Works Ltd
Contact: D'Arcy Gander
Unit 20, St Helena Farm, St Helena Lane
Plumpton Green, East Sussex, BN7 3DH
Tel: +44(0)1273 891777
www.vine-works.com

Vineyard Solutions
Contact: Ian Phillips
Baddow Park, West Hanningfield, Great
Baddow Chelmsford, Essex, CM2 7SY
Tel: +44 (0)1245 476994
www.vineyardsolutions.co.uk

Supplies – Winery

A E Chapman & Son Ltd
Contact: Rodger Boyd
Timbermill Way, Gauden Road, Clapham,
London, SW4 6LY
Tel: +44 (0)207 6224414
www.aechapman.co.uk

Bevtech Ltd
Contact: David Cowderoy
Moonhill Farm, Burgess Hill Road, Ansty
Haywards Heath, RH17 5AH
Tel: +44 (0)1444 41141
www.bevtech.co.uk

Core Equioment Ltd
Contact: Jonathan Chaplin
Unit 3, Everdon Park, Heartlands Business
Park Daventry, Northamptonshire,
NN11 8YJ
Tel: +44 (0)1327 342589
www.core-equip.com

Croxsons Ltd
Alpha Place, Garth Road, Morden
Surrey, SM4 4LX
Tel: +44 (0)208 3372945
www.croxsons.com

Erben Ltd
Contact: Mark Crumpton MSc
Lady Lane Industrial Estate, Hadleigh,
Ipswich IP7 6AS
Tel: +44 (0)1473 823011
www.erben.co.uk

Lallemand
Contact: Sigrid Gertsen-Schibbye
Bredstrupvej 33, 8500 Grenå, Denmark
Tel: +45 5357 2280
www.lallemandwine.com

Litmus Wines Ltd
London Road, Dorking, Surrey, RH5 6AA
Tel: +44 (0)1306 879829
www.litmuswines.com

N P Seymour Ltd
Avon Works, Cranbrook, Kent, TN17 2PT
Tel: +44 (0)1580 712200
www.npseymour.co.uk

Profil Solutions Ltd
Contact: Dave Manns
Units 1 & 2, Little Netherton, Dymock
Gloucestershire, GL18 2EF
Tel: +44 (0)1531 890809
www.profilsolutions.com

Rankin Brothers & Sons
Contact: Jim Rankin
3c Drakes Farm, Drakes Drive, Long
Crendon Buckinghamshire, HP18 9BA
Tel: +44 (0) 1844 203100
www.rankincork.co.uk

Vigo Ltd
Dunkeswell, Honiton, Devon, EX14 4LF
Tel: +44 (0)1404 892100
www.vigoltd.com

Supplies Vineyard

Agrovista UK Ltd
Contact: Alex Radu
Rutherford House, Nottingham Science
& Technology Park, University Boulevard
Nottingham, NG7 2PZ
Tel: +44 (0)115 939 0202
www.agrovista.co.uk

ArborAgri Ltd
Contact: Andrew Holbrow
Whiteway Head, Knowbury,
Ludlow, SY8 3LE
Tel: +44(0)1584 890913
www.arboragri.co.uk

ArcelorMittal Sheffield Ltd
Contact: Louise Walker
Vulcan Works, Birley Vale Close,
Sheffield, S12 2DB
Tel: +44(0)114 239 2601
www.arcelormittal.com/wiresolutions

Berthoud Sprayers Ltd
Contact: Martin Shackcloth
4 Oldmedow Road, Hardwick Industrial
Estate King's Lynn, Norfolk, PE30 4JJ
Tel: +44 (0)1553 774997
www.berthoud.co.uk

Calders & Grandidge Ltd
194 London Road, Boston, Lincs, PE21 7HJ
Tel: +44 (0)1205 358866
www.caldersandgrandidge.com

Capatex Ltd
Contact: Peter Strauss
127 North Gate, New Basford,
Nottingham NG7 7FZ
Tel: +44 (0)115 978 6111
www.growtex.co.uk

Greenbest Ltd
Contact: Simon Gillett
Unit 2, The Marsh, Henstridge,
Somerset, BA8 0TF
Tel: +44 (0)1963 364788
www.greenbest.co.uk

Gripple Ltd
The Old West Gun Works, 201 Savile Street
East Sheffield, S4 7UQ
Tel: +44(0)114 2288617
www.gripple.com

GT Products Ltd
Contact: Brett Adshead
Unit 14, Ford Lane Business Park,
Ford, Arundel, West Sussex, BN18 0UZ
Tel: +44 (0)1243 555 303
www.gtproductseurope.com

Horsepower UK Ltd
Contact: Polly Cook
Unit 2, Owens Court Farm, Selling,
Faversham ME13 9QN
Tel: +44 (0)1233 226284
www.horsepoweragri.co.uk

Hutchinsons Ltd
Contact: Chris Cooper
Weasenham Lane, Wisbech,
Cambridgeshire, PE13 2RN
Tel: +44 (0)1945 461177
www.hlhltd.co.uk

N P Seymour Ltd
Avon Works, Cranbrook, Kent, TN17 2PT
Tel: +44 (0)1580 712200
www.npseymour.co.uk

Platipus Anchors Ltd
Kingsfield Business Centre, Philanthropic
Road Redhill, Surrey, RH1 4DP
Tel: +44 (0)1737 762300
www.platipus-anchors.com

Richard Burton Specialised Machinery
Contact: Mike Burton
Folly Farm, Beck St, Hepworth, Diss,
Norfolk IP22 2PN
Tel: +44 (0)1359 250796
www.rbsm.me.uk

Southcott Vineyard
Contact: Tim Ingram Hill
Southcott House, Pewsey,
Wiltshire, SN9 5JP
Tel: +44 (0)1672 569190

Tubex Ltd
Contact: Simon Place
Berry Plastics, Blackwater Trading Estate
The Causeway, Maldon, CM9 4GG
Tel: +44 (0)1621 874201
www.tubex.com

Vigo Ltd
Dunkeswell, Honiton, Devon, EX14 4LF
Tel: +44 (0)1404 892100
www.vigoltd.com

Vine Care UK Ltd
Contact: Paul Woodrow-Hill
11 Penfolds Place, Arundel, West Sussex
BN18 9SA
Mobile: +44 (0) 7811 613141
www.vinecareuk.com

Vine Works Ltd
Contact: D'Arcy Gander
Unit 20, St Helena Farm, St Helena Lane
Plumpton Green, East Sussex, BN7 3DH
Tel: +44 (0)1273 891777
www.vine-works.com

Vineyard Solutions
Contact: Ian Phillips
Baddow Park, West Hanningfield, Great
Baddow Chelmsford, Essex, CM2 7SY
Tel: +44 (0)1245 476994
www.vineyardsolutions.co.uk

Vitifruit Equipment
Contact: David Sayell
Unit 3, Skitts Manor Farm, Moor Lane Marsh
Green, Kent, TN8 5RA
Tel: +44 (0)1732 866567
www.vitifruitequipment.co.uk

Index